LIFE SCIENCE LIBRARY

WEATHER

LIFE SCIENCE LIBRARY

CONSULTING EDITORS
René Dubos
Henry Margenau
C. P. Snow

WEATHER

by Philip D. Thompson, Robert O'Brien
and the Editors of LIFE

TIME INCORPORATED, NEW YORK

ABOUT THIS BOOK

SCIENTISTS of all fields agree that meteorology focuses upon the biggest, toughest and probably most exciting single subject of modern scientific inquiry: the more than four billion cubic miles of atmosphere whose turbulent movements make the world's varied weather. This book traces the basic circulation of heat and winds from equator to poles, and explains the many phenomena of weather, from hailstones to hurricanes. It describes how modern meteorologists, armed with such tools as radar, laser beams and computers, may change civilization itself as they make more accurate predictions and possibly modify the weather.

Each chapter of text is followed by a supplementary picture essay, although each may be read independently. For example, Chapter 7, "The Inexact Art of Forecasting," which describes the operations of the U.S. Weather Bureau, precedes a picture essay on "The Home Weatherman."

THE AUTHORS

PHILIP D. THOMPSON is associate director of the National Center for Atmospheric Research in Boulder, Colorado, and was named president of the American Meteorological Society for the term ending in January 1966. His career in meteorology includes work with the U.S. Air Force and the Institute for Advanced Study. Author of *Numerical Weather Analysis and Prediction*, he won the 1960 Meisinger Award for his research in this field.

ROBERT O'BRIEN, former newspaperman and columnist for the San Francisco *Chronicle*, now writes magazine articles on scientific subjects. He is the author of several books, including a previous volume in the LIFE Science Library, *Machines*.

THE CONSULTING EDITORS

RENE DUBOS, member and professor of The Rockefeller University, is a microbiologist and pathologist noted for his work in antibiotics. He is the author of *Mirage of Health* and *The Dreams of Reason*.

HENRY MARGENAU is a professor of physics and natural philosophy at Yale, author and eminent contributor to spectroscopy and nuclear physics. His books include *The Nature of Physical Reality*.

C. P. SNOW, physicist and author, has won acclaim for his many novels, which explore the relationship between the scientist and the rest of contemporary society. As Lord Snow, he was named to the British Ministry of Technology in 1964.

ON THE COVER

Three modern instruments swing in the breeze some 200 feet up a tower at Brookhaven National Laboratories on Long Island, measuring both wind speed and wind direction with new precision. The whorl of arrows on the back cover symbolizes spiraling storm winds.

CONTENTS

PAGE

INTRODUCTION 7

1 THE INGREDIENTS OF WEATHER 8
Picture Essay: Long-range Forecast—Variable 16

2 THE ATMOSPHERIC ENGINE 34
Picture Essay: Man against Hurricanes 42

3 WINDS OF THE WORLD 56
Picture Essay: Great Rivers of Air 66

4 THE SATURATED SKIES 80
Picture Essay: The Mechanics of Rainfall 90

5 AT THE WEATHER'S MERCY 106
Picture Essay: Meteorology in Miniature 114

6 LAWS OF THE ATMOSPHERE 126
Picture Essay: Myths, Deities and Computers 138

7 THE INEXACT ART OF FORECASTING 152
Picture Essay: The Home Weatherman 160

8 AN AWESOME FUTURE 172
Picture Essay: The New Science of Weather 180

APPENDIX 193
The Highs and Lows of U.S. Temperature
The Vocabulary of the Clouds

BIBLIOGRAPHY AND ACKNOWLEDGMENTS 196

INDEX 197

PICTURE CREDITS 200

TIME-LIFE BOOKS

EDITOR
Maitland A. Edey

TEXT DIRECTOR   ART DIRECTOR
Jerry Korn   Sheldon Cotler

CHIEF OF RESEARCH
Beatrice T. Dobie

Assistant Text Directors:
Harold C. Field, Ogden Tanner
Assistant Art Director: Arnold C. Holeywell
Assistant Chief of Research: Martha Turner

PUBLISHER
Rhett Austell

General Manager: Joseph C. Hazen Jr.
Circulation Director: Joan D. Manley
Marketing Director: Carter Smith
Business Manager: John D. McSweeney
Publishing Board: Nicholas Benton, Louis Bronzo,
James Wendell Forbes

LIFE MAGAZINE

EDITOR: Edward K. Thompson
MANAGING EDITOR: George P. Hunt
PUBLISHER: Jerome S. Hardy

LIFE SCIENCE LIBRARY

SERIES EDITOR: Martin Mann
Editorial staff for *Weather:*
Associate Editor: Robert G. Mason
Text Editors: Neal G. Stuart, Alfred Lansing,
Betsy Frankel
Designer: Arnold C. Holeywell
Associate Designer: Edwin Taylor
Staff Writers: Tom Alexander, Samuel Halper,
Jonathan Kastner, Charles Osborne
Chief Researcher: Thelma C. Stevens
Researchers: Doris C. Coffin, Robert W. Bone,
Edward Brash, Valentin Y. L. Chu, Mollie Cooper,
Rosemary Haverland, Donald Hinkle, Frank Kendig,
Donald Newton, Patricia Tolles, Victor H. Waldrop,
Carol Phillippe

EDITORIAL PRODUCTION
Color Director: Robert L. Young
Copy Staff: Marian Gordon Goldman,
Suzanne Seixas, Dolores A. Littles
Picture Bureau: Margaret K. Goldsmith,
Barbara Sullivan
Art Assistants: James D. Smith, Patricia Byrne,
Charles Mikolaycak, Douglas B. Graham

This book from its conception to final editing was under the professional direction of Philip D. Thompson. The text chapters were written by Robert O'Brien, the picture essays by the editorial staff. The following individuals and departments of Time Incorporated were helpful in the production of the book; LIFE staff photographers John Dominis, Alfred Eisenstaedt, Eliot Elisofon, Dmitri Kessel, Leonard McCombe, Carl Mydans, Arthur Rickerby; the Chief of the LIFE Picture Library, Doris O'Neil; the Chief of the TIME-LIFE News Service, Richard M. Clurman; and the Chief of the Time Inc. Bureau of Editorial Reference, Peter Draz.

INTRODUCTION

ANYONE WHO READS THE PAGES THAT FOLLOW can scarcely miss the air of excitement, the joy of discovery and the conviction of accomplishment that permeate the field of meteorology today. For several reasons, it is timely that the window behind which the atmospheric scientist and the professional meteorologist labor so assiduously be opened to the public view.

First, since all people suffer from the weather, benefit from the weather and support atmospheric research and weather forecasting, they have a right to know what it is all about. The meteorologist has a responsibility to tell them—as clearly and simply as it is done here.

Second, despite air-conditioned homes, automobiles and baseball stadiums, a growing population and an increasingly complex civilization are going to become more—not less—dependent on the vagaries of the ubiquitous atmosphere.

Third, advances in the pure science through which knowledge of the atmosphere is acquired, and progress in the applied science involving the use of that knowledge, are both taking place at such breathtaking speed that meteorology will be almost unrecognizable as we enter the 21st Century—when half of us can still expect to be alive. The guideposts Messrs. Thompson and O'Brien have set forth will help to make the adventuresome journey a fruitful one.

Fourth, while we are no closer to meaningful control of the weather than we were in the 1940s, the problem has subtly but perceptibly been transformed from the speculative phase to one that permits the rational and systematic exploration of possibilities and limitations. The implications of this development will require no further elaboration than that found in Chapter 8.

Finally, in a world shrunk by modern communication and transportation, beset with conflict and struggling with awesome decisions involving all mankind, there is an unparalleled opportunity to develop and perfect new patterns of international cooperation in the study and the use of an atmosphere that recognizes no national boundaries.

Weather is simply too important to be left to the meteorologists. It is a delight to invite you to share in its study, understanding and use.

—THOMAS F. MALONE
Chairman, Committee on Atmospheric Sciences
National Academy of Sciences - National Research Council

1
The Ingredients of Weather

TWO INESCAPABLE AND OFTEN EXASPERATING FACTS mark man's personal relations with the weather—with the state of the atmosphere as it was yesterday, as it is today, as it is likely to be tomorrow and in the near future.

One is that from his first breath to his last, it is always there. He may love it or hate it, revile it or resign himself to it; the one thing he cannot do is ignore it. Every morning there it is outside the window—raining or snowing, clear or cloudy, warm or cold. A bright, sparkling, autumn day of crisp air, blue skies, clear sunshine? He feels invigorated, stands straighter, strides more optimistically into his day. A sweltering summer morning? He feels irritable, depressed, exhausted before the day's work has fairly begun. Before he reaches the breakfast table, the weather colors and conditions man's physical well-being, the state of his emotions, his attitude toward life. Each day he takes it into account. Each day he lives by its grace, on its terms.

The other absolute is change. Whatever the state of the weather here and now, the one certainty is that it will not remain that way. Moreover, when it changes it will do so without even token reference to the needs or wishes of the humans in its path. As a heedless elephant scatters an ant hill, so a developing storm destined to paralyze Northern Europe next week will, en route, totally disrupt the lives of millions of Americans, playing havoc with their picnics and outings, their voyages and vacations, their arrivals and departures, their harvestings and homecomings. But, just as impersonally and with the same tantalizing caprice, it may come like a blessing, bringing unseasonable warmth amid the cold, refreshing sea breezes during the steaming days of summer, providing rain for thirsty lawns and crops, snow to ski on, fair winds for sailing, blue skies for flying.

The impact of weather strikes deeper than this.

A night fog drifts down over a busy turnpike, and a cautious driver slows down. A big truck roaring through the mist hits him from the rear; other vehicles, unable to stop, pile into the wreckage. Toll: many dead, more injured. A freak March storm forms off Cape Hatteras, travels up the Atlantic Coast, veers toward Newfoundland, stalls, sweeps its gale-force winds back across the Eastern Seaboard, then moves on once more to decay somewhere in the North Atlantic. Stunned residents count their losses: scores dead, thousands of homes and buildings destroyed, miles of beaches washed out to sea—damage estimated in the millions. A typhoon forms near Guam, spins across the Pacific, strikes first the Philippines, then Japan, and blows away to the northeast, leaving in its wake incalculable destruction and thousands dead. A sudden cold spell hits Florida—and half the state's citrus crop, mainstay of its agricultural economy, is frostbitten and rendered worthless. West of the Appala-

THE DAILY GENESIS OF WEATHER
This sunrise over Sleeping Bear Dunes in Michigan marks the beginning of the daily cycle of weather. While heat from the sun evaporates dew from gardens and lawns in Michigan, its energy is also driving the machinery of weather all over the world, soaking the tropics with rain, blanketing the Alps with snow—and perhaps generating a 200-mph storm off Cape Horn.

chians, it rains too hard and too long, and the Ohio River goes on a rampage; east of the Appalachians, it does not rain enough, and some 11 million people living in the New York metropolitan area have their water supplies rationed.

But all this may bring its own benefits. To cope with the vagaries of the weather, millions of Americans manufacture snow tires and bikinis, furnaces and raincoats, sunsuits and air conditioners: they fabricate golf clubs and patio furniture, run summer resorts in the Catskills and ski resorts in Colorado. Weather in its more benign form is the reason why one tenth of the nation lives in California, why the Southwest desert country is booming, why the multibillion-dollar space industry is burgeoning along the balmy Gulf Coast crescent.

The folk art of forecasting

Outdoorsmen have always had a special stake in tomorrow's weather. As a result, for thousands of years forecasting was a folk art practiced primarily by sailors, farmers, hunters, fishermen. They studied the clouds, felt the air's dampness on their cheek, noted a shift in the wind, added a certain tingling in their shoulder, an ache in the left femur, checked it with the behavior of cattle or birds, remembered pertinent sayings of their grandfathers, referred finally to their own experience and personal weather lore—and came up with an educated guess.

Though these methods were often amazingly accurate, weather has long since ceased to be a matter for chimney-corner experts. Today forecasting is a science called meteorology (from the Greek *meteoros*, high in the air, and *logos*, discourse). Federal spending on atmospheric research in the United States reached $170 million in 1963, and climbs higher every year.

Thanks to electronics and the space age, meteorologists now command the instruments and machines of an exciting technology that has discovered more about weather in the last 20 years than in all previous history.

Today a satellite with a television eye spies on hurricane clouds from above, and tells meteorologists how fast and in which direction they are moving. Balloons, tracked from the ground, reconnoiter the swift-flowing wind streams of the upper atmosphere. Rockets bore through the airless reaches of outer space with radiation-measuring devices that send their data streaming earthward in telemetered radio signals. On earth itself, electronic computers that can perform a million calculations a second assimilate information from hundreds of observation points all over the globe, sorting it, sifting it, following the instructions contained in intricate equations—and printing out, finally, the probable pattern of the upper atmosphere of the entire Northern Hemisphere for a complete 24-

hour period. This is a projection that would have been impossible 20 years ago, but it is now considered merely a routine preliminary to scientific forecasting.

All weather begins with four primary interacting elements. One is the sun, source of light and life, whose radiant energy ultimately determines the state of the atmosphere. Second comes the earth itself, whose unique geometry dictates the distinctive characteristics of weather and climate. The next element is the earth's atmosphere (from the Greek *atmos*, vapor, and *sphaira*, sphere), the envelope of gases which modulates solar radiation in its passage to earth. The fourth factor that shapes the weather is made up of the natural landforms and geophysical features of the earth's surface—the mountains, valleys, oceans, ice caps, deserts, lakes and rivers that alter the state of much of the atmosphere as it swirls incessantly around the globe.

The first of these influences on the weather, the sun, is a yellow-white star 865,000 miles in diameter and some 93 million miles from the earth. It is a fiery ball of exploding gases whose outer, luminous layer, or photosphere, registers temperatures as high as 10,000° Fahrenheit, and whose inner core is a flaming chaos where the heat may reach an unimaginable 30,000,000°. In volume, the sun is 1,306,000 times as large as the earth. Its weight is an estimated two billion billion billion tons, some 333,420 times that of the earth. If the universe were shrunk until the earth was the size and weight of a table-tennis ball, the sun would still measure some 12 and a half feet in diameter and it would weigh approximately three tons.

A hydrogen furnace

The central fact about the sun with relation not only to weather on earth but to all forms of life on earth is that it is a stupendous thermonuclear power plant. In this vast furnace, fusion "burns" hydrogen and converts it into helium. In the process the sun transforms part of its substance into energy that it radiates at the constant rate of 70,000 horsepower for every square yard of its vast and seething surface. To stoke this nuclear furnace the sun destroys four million tons of its own mass every second. It has been consuming itself at this rate for five billion years; it has the resources to keep it up, at the current rate, for at least 30 billion more.

If the sun's heat dropped by 13 per cent, it is estimated that the entire earth would soon be encased in a layer of ice a mile thick; if its heat increased by as much as 30 per cent, it would cook every vestige of life off the face of the planet.

Of the vast amount of energy that the sun radiates into space, the earth intercepts only a tiny fraction—about one two-billionth. Yet this fraction pours onto the earth a steady, unceasing 23 trillion horsepower —more energy every minute than all of mankind uses, in all forms, in one year. The sun beams this energy through space to earth as electromagnetic waves of three kinds, all of which are similar to radio waves, but shorter in length (an electromagnetic wave is measured, not the way an ocean wave is, from trough to crest, but by the distance between crests). The first kind, the ultraviolet rays, measure from 400 billionths to about 16 millionths of an inch in length; the second, the infrared rays, measure from 30 millionths to 400 thousandths of an inch (the short wave of radio, by comparison, measures several feet in length). Neither the ultraviolet nor the infrared rays can be seen by the human eye. In between them lie the wavelengths of visible light, ranging from 16 millionths of an inch (violet) to 30 millionths of an inch (red).

The method by which the sun's radiation is turned into heat will be discussed in detail later, but it is roughly comparable to the way a stone used to be transformed into a foot warmer in pioneer days. The stone absorbed energy radiated by the campfire. Then, placed inside the bedroll, it reradiated this energy as heat and gave the pioneer a snug, comfortable bed to look forward to. In similar fashion the earth absorbs radiant energy from the sun (the process is called "insolation"), is warmed by it, and reradiates this energy, in the form of heat, into its encompassing blanket of atmosphere.

An important change occurs in the process. The wavelengths of terrestrial radiation going out are longer than those of insolation coming in—too long to escape or to bounce back readily through the atmosphere into space. Much of this radiation is absorbed by the water vapor in the atmosphere. It is this heat energy, garnered from the sun in the equatorial and temperate zones, that powers the complex circulation of the atmosphere, that drives the winds, brews the cyclones and hurricanes, sets the sky to crackling with lightning bolts, creates and showers down on earth the blessed rains and furious snows that so directly affect man's existence.

The earth's contribution

Of course, the earth is not entirely at the meteorological mercy of the sun. As a member of the solar family, it has unique features of its own that contribute profoundly to the creation of its weather.

One is the fact that in addition to its annual 600-million-mile swing around the sun in its elliptical orbit, the earth rotates on its own axis, from west to east, at a speed at the equator of nearly 1,050 miles an hour. This west-to-east rotation also determines the prevailing direction of persistent winds and the prevailing direction of ocean currents, both of which contribute to making the weather what it is.

THE SUN CASTS SHADOWS that vary in length depending on the season, reflecting changes in the earth-sun relationship that cause seasonal variations in weather. The drawings show the shadows cast by a stick near Boston at about the time of the winter solstice, when the sun is farthest south *(left)*; at the spring and autumn equinoxes *(center)*, when day and night *(shaded area)* have the same length; and at the summer solstice, when the sun is farthest north. The shadows lengthen in autumn and winter because the Northern Hemisphere is tilted away from the sun, decreasing the angle at which the sun's rays strike, and bringing shorter days and colder weather. In spring and summer, the sun's rays strike more directly and the weather warms up.

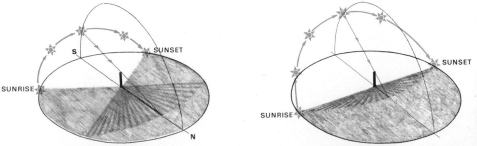

DECEMBER 21   MARCH 21 AND SEPTEMBER 23

12

Another feature of the earth that influences weather is its shape. Isaac Newton, in the 17th Century, proclaimed the earth an oblate spheroid —a ball, flattened at the poles—and modern geodesy, with the help of photographic measurements from artificial satellites, confirms the fact. This roughly spherical shape makes for sharp differences in the temperature in different parts of the earth. Just as a flashlight beam makes a sharp bright spot when it strikes a surface at right angles, but spreads out and dims when it strikes a surface angled away from it, so the sun's rays strike with greater intensity at some parts of the earth than at others. The intensity of solar radiation is further affected by the fact that on a slanting course the sun's rays must travel through more of the atmosphere, and are thus more completely absorbed before reaching the earth.

Still another peculiarity of the earth's situation in space is its tilt with relation to the plane of its path around the sun. It is canted at a fixed angle of $23\frac{1}{2}°$. This slant further modifies the angle at which the sun's rays strike the earth. It also accounts for four seasons, because entire areas of the earth are tipped toward or away from the sun for half a year at a time. Thus, in January, that same square foot of land at Anchorage receives only 9 per cent as much solar energy as it does in July. But in the Southern Hemisphere in January the sun is striking with full force; in that part of the globe the coolest part of the year comes during the northern summer.

The atmospheric blanket

Here, then, are two of the quantities that produce weather—that celestial furnace the sun and, 93 million miles away, the circling, tilted planet earth. There is a third element essential not only to the existence of weather, but to the existence of life itself. That is the invisible and indispensable stuff called the atmosphere. Without it, the earth would be a dead planet, as sterile and lifeless as the moon; there would be no trees, no animals or birds, no bright sky, no clouds or golden sunsets. Not only is it essential because all life breathes it; it is also a necessary protective blanket. Without it, the rays of the sun would scorch the earth's crust with temperatures as high as 180° F. by day at the equator. By night, the cold would reach an unendurable 220° below zero at the same place.

The atmosphere is a fluid mixture of gases surrounding the earth, encasing it in concentric layers of varying thickness and density. Insubstantial as it seems, it has ponderous mass. Held to earth by gravity, it has a total weight of at least 5,600 trillion tons. At sea level, a vertical column of air one inch square and extending to the outer reaches of the atmosphere weighs 14.7 pounds; a column a foot square weighs more

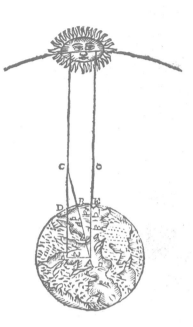

SUNLIGHT and its distribution over the earth are shown in this 17th Century illustration from a book by the German scientist Athanasius Kircher. Although he erred in having his sun revolve about the earth, Kircher, using geometry, determined accurately which parts of the globe would be light and which parts would be dark at a given time of the year.

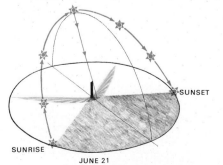

SUNRISE

SUNSET

JUNE 21

13

than a ton. On each human at sea level, depending on his size and the area of his skin surface, the atmosphere exerts a crushing pressure of from 10 to 20 tons. Men survive at the bottom of this sea just as fish survive at the bottom of theirs: inner body pressure, pushing out, equalizes atmospheric pressure pushing in. And to carry the comparison with the salt-water ocean one step further, the atmosphere, like the ocean, is heavier at its bottom, thinning out rapidly with increasing distance from the earth's surface. The air pressure that reaches nearly 15 pounds per square inch at sea level diminishes to only seven and a half pounds at 18,000 feet. Though its most rarefied frontier is hundreds or even thousands of miles out in space, all but 1 per cent of the atmosphere lies in a layer 19 miles thick around the earth.

Water in the air

The atmosphere is composed mainly of oxygen and nitrogen, but it also contains minute quantities (about .03 per cent) of carbon dioxide, which plays an important role in stabilizing temperatures both near the earth's surface and in the upper atmosphere. Various other substances are present as well—most notably, water vapor.

Water is, meteorologically, the most important constituent of the atmosphere of the earth. It is present up to altitudes of about 40,000 to 45,000 feet, in amounts ranging from about zero over some mountains and deserts to 4 per cent over oceans and seas. If all of it were condensed in liquid form, it would cover the entire surface of the earth with one inch of rainfall.

Water exists in the atmosphere in three forms: as an invisible, gaseous vapor; as liquid droplets, and as solid ice crystals. In the two latter states, it comprises visible precipitation—rain, hail, sleet, snow.

The atmosphere wraps the earth in several distinct layers. First and lowest is the troposphere. The troposphere's thickness varies from five miles at the poles to 10 miles at the equator. Tropospheric air is heavy, its molecules densely packed. Though the troposphere constitutes a small fraction of the total depth of the atmosphere, it contains 80 per cent of the total weight and virtually all the water vapor. It is the planetary caldron of weather. Within the troposphere, humid air, heated by the ground beneath, boils heavenward at the equator, creating vast, tropical updrafts. To the far north, ponderous masses of dry cold air sink earthward. Horizontal wind currents howl across the icefield at tremendous speeds. Surface temperatures, ranging from more than 100° F. over oceans and deserts to as much as 100° below zero at the poles, create a churning in the atmosphere that determines weather and weather patterns all around the world. In the troposphere temperature decreases with altitude at an average rate of 3.6° F. for every thousand feet—that is, with increasing distance from the source of atmospheric heat, the sun-warmed earth.

In addition to the sun, the earth's geometry and the atmosphere, one final factor influences the weather. That is the earth's geophysical land-form—the mountain barriers, the oceans, the continents, the valleys, the lakes. What the weather is in any area today, or next month, depends a great deal on that region's landforms.

Land, for instance, both gains and loses heat more quickly than water does. Since water retains heat longer than soil, people living near a sea-coast or large inland body of water experience cooler summers and mild-er winters than those who live far from the nearest ocean or lake. A resi-dent of central New York State may board a plane for Boston, leaving behind several feet of snow and sub-zero temperatures, and discover that on the Atlantic Coast, in the same latitude, the weather is so mild that there is not even ice for skating. Similarly, the traveler who leaves Fargo, North Dakota, in the middle of June, with temperatures pushing 90°, may, several days later, be shivering on the deck of a transatlantic steamer in precisely the same latitude—because the ocean still retains the icy chill of winter. Thanks to bracing winds off the cool Pacific, some 800,000 San Franciscans may work and sleep in the comfortable 60s in July while 90 miles north, in the breezeless oven of the Sacramento Valley, temperatures soar toward a baking 110° in the shade.

Millions of people living along thousands of miles of coastlines benefit from this physical contiguity of land and water. It accounts for a cool sea breeze off the water during the day, and for the breeze that blows seaward off the land at night—major characteristics of the coastal weath-er pattern that, particularly in the tropics, makes life healthier and more pleasant than it would otherwise be. Sometimes it brings chill nights to even the most torrid locations. In Fiji, people often are forced to don overcoats at night for protection against the sudden cold.

The influence of mountains

Mountain ranges are also among the dynamic determinants of local and regional weather. In the United States, for example, the Mississippi Valley and Great Plains lie like a continental trough between the Rockies in the West and the Appalachians in the East. Wintry blasts from the north sweep down this trough as through a funnel. Clashing with warm, moist air from the Gulf, they generate the massive, eastward-moving storms and blizzards that frequently paralyze the densely populated areas of the nation. But mountain barriers can also protect a region from air movements that bring stormy weather. Along the French Riviera, the Maritime Alps shut out cold north winds. The result is year-round balmy weather, with scarcely a touch of frost even in January. Mean-

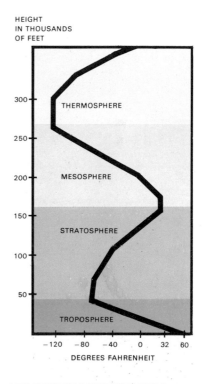

HEIGHT IN THOUSANDS OF FEET

ATMOSPHERIC TEMPERATURE, contrary to popular belief, does not drop steadily as altitude increases. It does fall from ground level to the top of the troposphere, but in the stratosphere it rises—affected by the heat-absorbent form of oxygen called ozone. In the ozone-free mesosphere the air cools. In the thermosphere it rises again.

while, Portland, Maine, in the same latitude but with the stormy North Atlantic on its doorstep, may have snow for half the year.

The most dramatic example of the effect of mountain ranges on regional weather, perhaps, is the orographic, or mountain-modified, wind which is discussed in greater detail later. In brief, this is generally a prevailing wind that crosses a high mountain barrier. As it ascends, it cools and its water vapor condenses into precipitation. On the other side of the mountain, deprived of its moisture, it reaches the valley floor as a hot, eye-stinging, throat-parching wind accompanied by other phenomena: a strange, crystalline clarity of air, extraordinary visibility, and lens-shaped clouds that form high in the air and to the leeward side of the ridge.

Everywhere in the world, whatever its beginning, whether affected by mountains or oceans, the weather exerts a powerful influence on mankind.

It can be a shattering force of ruin and desolation. But it also can be a patch of soft spring sky, a pattering of rain on thirsty leaves, a witchery of fog across the hills, a silence of snow over the city. Either way, it is part of man's life—a never-ending, ever-changing pageant created by sun, air and earth. It still has its mysteries, its secrets. But they are dwindling. Under the assault of science, they are fewer today than ever before.

Long-range Forecast— Variable

The essence of weather is change. In minutes, the sea can turn from brilliant calm to towering storm (*opposite*). A shift in the wind can change an Indian summer's day to a real foretaste of winter, ominous with clouds and bitterly cold. In hurricane season, the storm that tore through Key West yesterday may smash New England next week—or dissipate harmlessly in the North Atlantic. The same wet Pacific wind that dumps tons of snow on the western slopes of the Rockies slides down the mountains' eastern slopes as the warm, dry zephyr that thaws the snowbound prairies. From day to day, or within the longer swings of seasonal change, man may be hurt by flood or drought, cheered by healing rain or morning dew, terrified by hurricane, blizzard or tornado—all because the earth is cloaked in a veil of atmosphere which is seemingly insubstantial, but whose constant movements affect him every moment of his life.

SUN-GILDED STORM CLOUDS
In a dramatic illustration of the changing nature of weather, the towering clouds of an early-evening rainstorm obscure the sun off Bermuda. This photograph also illustrates the cyclical nature of weather involving sun, air and water. Heat from the sun evaporates water, which forms clouds. The clouds cool and eventually return the water to earth in one form of precipitation or another.

16

The Prime Movers: Fire and Ice

Over the tropic sea near the Hawaiian Islands, the blistering sun beats down day after day, heating the air, evaporating the ocean water. Half a world away, the frozen poles are covered with ancient ice. At any given moment the temperature differential between these thermal extremes may be as much as 180° F. The air distance that separates them is some 12,000 miles. Yet, remote as these areas of the planet are from each other, there is an unceasing interchange between them: through the medium of the atmosphere, tropic winds are constantly transferring their heat to cooler air masses coming from the poles. This heat transfer is the fundamental cause of all the varieties of weather shown on the following pages.

SUNSET OVER THE NORTH PACIFIC

A FROZEN ICE FIELD IN ANTARCTICA

18

DEW SPARKLES ON A WOODLAND PLANT

FROST CLOTHES OAK LEAVES AND FERNS

FOG FILTERS THROUGH AN ENGLISH FOREST

The Evening Dews and Damps

Water vapor—gaseous and invisible—is always present in the atmosphere, even in the air over the poles and the driest deserts. At various times and places it may condense as the result of cooling, which can occur in a number of ways. The least spectacular takes place at the very surface of the earth. With the coming of night, the ground yields up the day's heat. The temperature of the earth drops, and airborne water vapor condenses to form either dew or frost, depending on the degree of cold. Closely akin to these two is fog, which is condensation, not on the surface of the earth, but on invisible particles in the air.

The Spectacle of Cloud and Rain

A single thunderstorm *(bottom)* is a spectacle. But when they are massed into an ominous advancing squall line *(top)*, thunderstorms assume the terrifying appearance of a huge black tidal wave. A squall line, composed of dozens of thunderstorms, is similar to a rank of soldiers advancing abreast. These storms are a meteorological mystery. They form, no one knows why, 50 to 250 miles in front of a cold front that is pushing into warm, muggy air. Like a shock wave, the squall line strikes, usually with violent winds and rain—and 20 minutes later has passed on, leaving the weather exactly as it was before. But squall lines are one of weather's surest signs of change. Within hours, cold air will follow and overrun the region.

A SQUALL LINE BEARS DOWN ON
PATRICK AIR FORCE BASE IN FLORIDA (TOP)

AS IF ON AN IMMENSE STAGE, A DARK CURTAIN OF RAIN
CLOSES ACROSS A FIELD IN SOUTHERN NEW MEXICO

Rain Measured by the Foot

The coming of rain to the monsoon belt of Southeast Asia is among the most dramatic natural phenomena. For six months, roughly from January to June, dry winds blowing from the northeast off the Gobi Desert parch the region, sucking moisture from the soil. Then one blessed day in June, sometimes in the space of only an hour, the wind may veer a full 180°, and begin to sweep inland from the southwest, bearing with it moisture off the Indian Ocean and the Bay of Bengal. These cool, moist monsoon winds, moving across the scorched earth, are suddenly pushed upward by convection currents. The result is rain, often in torrential amounts. At Cherrapunji, near the Burmese border, average annual rainfall is 436 inches—more than 36 feet.

PILGRIMS GATHER AT A RELIGIOUS FESTIVAL TO GIVE THANKS FOR THE MONSOON RAINS

The Curse of
Too Much Water

Weather in excess often brings disaster. Wild winds can ravage coasts. Blizzards may paralyze vast areas. And rain in amounts too great for the land to handle may cause floods.

In a few cases, floods may be beneficial, such as the yearly flooding of the Nile that follows the runoff of melted snows from the Ruwenzori Range and spring rains. Other annual floods, notably in the Midwest, are often of disaster proportions.

But the most devastating floods are the terrible flash floods, which follow violent rainstorms. The damage and death caused by such floods results from the fact that they are unexpected. In 1955, New England was caught by a downpour that brought 14 inches of rain in one day. The Connecticut River rose 19½ feet, pouring over its banks. When the storm had passed, 186 people were dead, and property damage was over two billion dollars.

HUNTER RIVER VALLEY, AUSTRALIA

FEATHER RIVER WATERS IN YUBA CITY, CALIFORNIA

MAHANADI RIVER, INDIA

27

A TOWERING TEXAS DUST STORM

THE CRACKED MUD BED OF A CALIFORNIA RIVER

The Scorching Assault of Drought

The face of dry weather is harsh. Its cruelty is revealed on these pages *(from left)* in the deep, malignant red of a dust storm in the American West, the metallic glare of an Egyptian desert, the tortured fissures in an empty river bed. The winds of drought are carriers of dust and sand, and local people often give them proper names, like personal enemies. Egypt has the *haboob*, a wind that lifts dust to great heights. Arabia's windy plague is the *shamal*, which drives sand through the air at 40 miles per hour. The horror of this storm has been brilliantly described by T. E. Lawrence. In the "breathless wind," he wrote, "our faces chapped, while our eyelids, gone granular, seemed to creep back and bare our shrinking eyes."

29

STORM-DRIVEN WAVES BATTER THE WATERFRONT OF PROVINCETOWN, MASSACHUSETTS, IN AUGUST 1954

The Atmosphere's Safety Valve

A man beset by a great storm such as the one shown above lambasting Provincetown, Massachusetts, thinks of the storm's explosion as purposeless and destructive. But to a meteorologist, even the most destructive storm has a purpose: the release of excess energy through a safety valve.

Just as a ship's boiler would explode if steam pressure were allowed to build up indefinitely, so energy released by the interaction of hot and cold air would reach fantastic levels if it did not dissipate regularly. Then, when it did explode, the resulting storm would be utterly catastrophic.

31

Fossilized Weather, Centuries Old

Changes in weather usually occur quickly. The life of a storm is measured in days, and even the great seasonal weather variations take place in the course of one journey of the earth around the sun. And so it is difficult to imagine the perennial snows of the last ice age, when for 470,000 unbroken years a mantle of glaciers covered one quarter of the earth.

But the glaciers that remain, such as the majestic Alaskan giant shown at right, are spectacular reminders of that ice age. Here is century upon century of winter—1,100 feet thick, 20 miles long, four miles wide. Shoved by the pressure of accumulated snow and ice, and by the slope of the land, the glacier inches toward the sea. There, snow crystals that fell 1,000 years ago drop as icebergs into the ocean and resume a liquid form at last.

EROSION MARKS THE 300-FOOT-HIGH CLIFFS
OF THE TAKU GLACIER, NEAR JUNEAU

2
The Atmospheric Engine

Sᴜɴ, ᴇᴀʀᴛʜ ᴀɴᴅ ᴀᴛᴍᴏsᴘʜᴇʀᴇ together constitute a stupendous engine for the production of weather. The sun is the furnace, turning fuel into radiant energy. The earth's warmer regions are the boiler, where the energy is converted into useful heat. The heat sets the giant envelope of atmosphere in motion, to perform the work that we call weather.

What sort of work does the atmosphere do? It is an extravagantly inefficient machine: only 3 per cent of the energy it receives is converted into energy of motion. Yet this is more than enough to move things about. In Trowbridge, England, a man running in from a heavy storm heard sounds as of mud plopping on the pavement behind him. He turned around and saw hundreds of tiny frogs falling from the sky. A thunderstorm in Providence, Rhode Island, delivered live fish, strewing them over a quarter of an acre. A storm in Worcester, England, in 1881, poured crabs and periwinkles into the streets by the sackful. This storm has a particularly respected place in the annals of meteorology, for Worcester is 40 miles from the sea.

Transporting periwinkles 40 miles through the air is the kind of work the atmosphere does with ease. It does more difficult work as well. It is perpetually moving its own weight of some 5,600 trillion tons, some of it at jet-stream speeds of 200 to 400 miles an hour. The estimated 500 million tons of topsoil borne off by the wind during a single storm in Nebraska and South Dakota seem trivial compared with the quantities of water the atmosphere carries at all times. A single small, fluffy cloud may hold from 100 to 1,000 tons of moisture. On a hot afternoon, the atmosphere evaporates water from the Gulf of Mexico at the rate of 5.5 billion gallons an hour, hoists it up and carries it off to the northeast by the millions of tons, to release it later as rain over New York and southern New England. A polar air mass moving south from Canada may pick up nine gallons of water from the Mississippi drainage basin for every gallon that flows from the mouth of the Mississippi River itself. It may then carry this moisture over the Gulf and dump it as rain to even the account for what was removed earlier.

The energy involved in these atmospheric chores is prodigious. A summer thunderstorm squanders in its profligate lifetime as much energy as a dozen or so Hiroshima-type bombs—and 45,000 thunderstorms are brewed around the earth every day. A hurricane releases almost as much energy in one second. Weather, whether it hurtles periwinkles, blows down houses or merely bends the grass, is the display of energy.

Weather has a reputation for being capricious, but like all manifestations of energy, it follows physical laws. Local and even global weather predictions are difficult partly because the engine creating weather is so huge and has such a profusion of parts. But we have weather in the first place because of a basic principle of physics: energy is convertible with-

HEAT AT THE TOP
An otherwise blue Pacific is marked by a patch of clouds in this picture taken 100 miles up by an Astronaut. An island beneath the clouds radiates much more heat into the air than the surrounding water does. As the air rises and cools, its water vapor condenses into clouds. In microcosm, this illustrates the heating, lifting and condensation that produce weather.

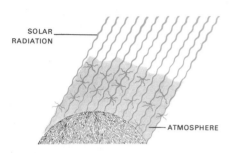

SOLAR RADIATION, which creates weather, is acted upon in several ways by the earth. In the diagram above, it is scattered by air, dust and water vapor. More blue light is dispersed than any other color, accounting for the tint of the sky.

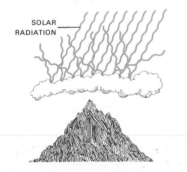

INCOMING RADIATION is reflected back into space by clouds and the earth's surface. Clouds turn back some 25 per cent of all incoming radiation. Part of this is visible from outer space as a brilliant glow, or "earthshine," of blues, greens and whites.

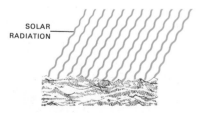

ABSORBED RADIATION, about half of the total, is converted into heat upon striking the earth. This heat evaporates water from the oceans and warms the lower atmosphere, thereby providing the essential ingredients that produce the world's weather.

out loss. That is, energy may take many forms, changing from radiation to heat to motion, but it cannot be destroyed.

Solar energy, discussed in detail in the preceding chapter, is composed of radiations in many different wavelengths. Some 23 trillion horsepower reaches the earth's upper atmosphere continuously. As the assorted wavelengths pass through the atmosphere, they meet varying fates. Some are scattered as they bounce off molecules of air, water droplets or microscopic particles of dust. Other rays carom intact off the tops of clouds and are reflected back into space. Nearly half the incoming solar energy is lost to earth by reflection.

But more than half the supply of energy is still available to be absorbed. Air is a poor absorber of radiant energy, and only 15 per cent of the solar energy is absorbed by elements in the atmosphere—by dust and certain atmospheric gases such as water vapor, ozone and carbon dioxide.

The rest finally reaches man's level. Much of it is in the form of light. It has traveled 93 million miles, performing, as far as we know, very little work along the way. But now it strikes the many surfaces of earth—a body of water, a furrowed field, a leaf, a cheek. Highly reflective surfaces like a polar ice cap or a glass skyscraper turn some of it back with a blinding glare, adding to the total reflected back into space. Some of it also is absorbed by plants and used in the chemically complex processes of growth. But most of the surfaces absorb it—and put it to work at last.

The radiant energy is converted into the energy of molecular motion. As the sun's radiation strikes houses, people, land and oceans it sets molecules dancing. This is the form of energy we call heat. The faster an object's molecules move, the warmer it feels to the touch. At absolute zero ($-459.69°$ F.) there would be no molecular motion. The molecules of an ice cube are relatively quiescent. But a tin roof on a sunny day is an invisible tempest of molecular activity. As its molecules move, continually receiving more energy, they throw off some of it in the form of long infrared rays. Thus all over the earth, various surfaces transform the sun's short waves into long infrared waves, which excite any molecules that intervene into increased activity. These are felt as radiant heat. The earth itself is thus transformed into a giant radiator of heat.

Engineered for confusion

But unlike a sensibly engineered radiator, the earth radiates heat unevenly. Rivers, mountains, shores and plains cause local differences in heat production. Boston swelters while Cape Cod registers a pleasant 70°F. Denver remains warm while blizzards rage on the mountaintops a few miles away. On a global scale, winter and summer, day and night, the land and the oceans, the equatorial regions and the polar regions all cause temperatures to rise and fall at different times, in different places—and this causes complications for meteorologists.

The uneven distribution of heat sets the great machinery of the atmosphere in motion. The net effect of this motion is to distribute the heat more evenly around the world. This, as simply as anything, summarizes the plot of the drama of weather. Warm and less warm air move and mix—vertically, horizontally, often turbulently, in all directions. In broad strokes, warm equatorial air moves toward the poles, and cold air from the poles moves toward the equator. This basic movement creates our intercontinental winds and systems of weather. The balmy air of a January day in California was warmed over the mid-Pacific, a cold snap in New Jersey began over the barren ground of Canada.

The puzzle of heat

For centuries the nature of heat was one of the great puzzles of the natural world, and all sorts of experiments have contributed to the solution of its mysteries. Probably the earliest men to build fires noted that smoke rises, and common observation also taught that warm air mixes with and gives some of its heat to cooler air. The early Greeks knew that air expands as it grows warmer and contracts with cooling.

Galileo Galilei, applying this principle, invented the first thermometer about 1600. His "thermoscope" consisted of a thin glass tube a foot and a half long. It was blown into an egg-sized bulb at one end, but was open at the other. Galileo warmed the bulb in his hands, then placed the open end in water. As the bulb cooled, the air inside contracted, and water pushed partway up the tube. From this level, the column of water rose or fell with every change of temperature. With the addition of an arbitrary scale, it became a crude thermometer. Later experimenters refined it and created the standard scales that are now in use.

By the 18th Century, the properties of heat were being seriously studied. Scientists used concave mirrors to focus the rays from a heat source and beam them across a room, sometimes as far as 24 feet away, magically igniting a spoonful of sulphur or a small pile of tinder. One scientist found by careful measurement that it takes longer to bring water to a boil in a brightly scoured pot than in one whose outside surface is blackened with soot. His explanation was that a shiny pot reflects "particles of fire" —not a bad approximation of the truth, which is that a shiny surface reflects heat, while a blackened one absorbs it.

The results were all very puzzling. Heat moved invisibly through space, it traveled in straight lines and it could be reflected. The theory was widely held that heat was an invisible substance, called "caloric," that flowed from a warm body into a cooler until equilibrium was reached.

In 1798, however, an American Tory expatriate, Benjamin Thompson, later Count Rumford, brought the caloric theory into question. He had noticed, in the course of his military career, the intense heat generated by friction when brass cannons were bored by drills. He had a brass cylinder drilled under gallons of water whose temperature was 60°F., and much to the astonishment of spectators, the water eventually came to a rolling boil. It was hard to believe that sufficient "caloric" could have been squeezed out of the brass to boil water. The cylinder and bored-out scrap were carefully weighed; together they weighed precisely the same as the intact cylinder before boring commenced. Moreover, the supply of heat had been apparently inexhaustible. This, to Count Rumford, was the most significant point of all. He declared firmly, "Anything which any insulated body . . . can continually furnish without limitation, cannot possibly be a material substance." Heat could not be "caloric"; he strongly suspected that it was related instead to the movement of the drill biting into brass.

In the 19th Century, a succession of physicists began exploring the connection Rumford had hypothesized between heat and motion. An English physicist, James Joule, raised the temperature of water by churning it with paddle wheels. While on his honeymoon in the Swiss Alps, he was seen gingerly climbing a mountain while carrying a large, specially constructed thermometer—so he could measure the temperature of a waterfall at both the top and the bottom of its fall. Joule helped prove conclusively that Count Rumford was right. Heat was soon determined to be the manifestation of molecular motion. And the study of modern meteorology is the study of how this molecular motion generates the movement of winds and all the other work that weather performs— which in turn helps distribute heat to all the quarters of the globe.

A watery trap for heat

Earth's weather can be said to begin around the earth's middle. The tropics receive vastly more solar energy per square mile than the polar caps. If all the earth's atmosphere were clear and dry, the heat radiated from all the earth's surfaces, including that from the tropics, would pass very quickly back into space. But three quarters of the earth's surface consists of water, and the skies overhead are loaded with water vapor to varying degrees. This water vapor is a special blessing, indispensable for life on earth. Although oxygen and nitrogen are poor absorbers of energy, water is a good one. Heat emanating from land and ocean is absorbed in abundance by vapor and cloud droplets, and reradiated back to earth.

This giant tennis game played with infrared rays is called by meteorologists the "greenhouse" effect, for water in the air performs somewhat the same function as the glass roof of a greenhouse: it lets through incoming light and ultraviolet rays, but traps outgoing infrared waves. Thus the equatorial regions in particular become a kind of giant boiler room, building up more heat than they radiate off into space. The heat's ultimate outlet is in the polar regions, which send back into space more radiant energy than they originally receive from the sun. Eventually, every bit of the earth's daily receipt of solar energy is restored to space; the earth's average temperature remains a constant 57°F. But the surplus heat from the boiler stays on earth long enough to go to work before it escapes, making the earth's northern and southern latitudes more equable.

Movable stores of energy

Water-soaked atmosphere not only bounces infrared radiation back to earth, it also stores energy. Water vapor, moved by winds, is one of the atmosphere's most important vehicles for the transportation of heat. As solar energy strikes and penetrates water, the water is warmed below, but the exposure to energy on the surface is particularly intense. The millions of tons of water borne aloft from the Gulf of Mexico represent untold numbers of molecules set in such violent motion that they are torn free from their fellows, or evaporated. In other words, they have absorbed enough energy to keep other molecules at a distance; and the liquid water is converted to a gas.

This vapor exists in some degree in all skies. The vast amount of energy it carries is called "latent heat," because it converts back into heat when the vapor condenses back into a liquid. Every time air is cooled sufficiently, its vapor condenses into clouds, composed of tiny water droplets—and heat is released into the atmosphere.

Air from the coldest northern seas bears a small amount of this latent energy. The moisture in a Maine sleet storm represents some of the solar energy that reached waters off Labrador. The storm is apt to be brief, and the heat it releases is lost high above the earth.

The moisture-laden winds from the south, however, shed vast amounts of latent heat as they move north; as they cool off they precipitate heavy rains and snows. (The heaviest snowfalls in the U.S. occur when the temperature is between 24° and 30°F.) One meteorologist has calculated that an inch of rain over an area releases as much energy as three days of sunshine falling in the same area.

Moist air, then, carries great stores of latent heat. It is the work of the heat engine to spread this supply about. The atmosphere performs this task of heat exchange by sheer movement—known as convection.

Man has always known that air moves, and that hot air moves upward. Today we know that air moves because some parts of it have more energy than others—i.e., are hotter than others. As air is warmed, its molecules become agitated and push away from one another. The air expands. As it expands, its population of molecules per cubic inch becomes less. Atmospheric pressure at any given point is the measurement of the total

GALILEO'S PROTEGES, Vincenzio Viviani and Evangelista Torricelli, organized the Academy of Experiments in Florence. There, eminent Florentine scientists carried out notable experiments in the measurement of temperature and atmospheric pressure. The instruments *(foreground)* were made for the Academy by the famous Florentine glassblowers, and included an intricate and accurate spiral thermometer *(left)*, and *(second from right)* an early hygrometer.

weight of air above it. Because of its lesser density, a column of hot air weighs less than an equal column of cold air, exerting less pressure. As hot air expands, the cooler air next to it, under greater pressure, pushes sideways, forcing the warmer air in the only direction it can go—up.

Differences in temperature create imbalances in pressure, and unless an extraneous factor intervenes—a Himalayan peak, for example— horizontal imbalances in pressure cause an inexorable flow of air from the area of higher pressure to the area of lower pressure. In a small room with a pot-bellied stove in the middle of it, this flow becomes a neat, self-sustaining cycle. The air around the stove is pushed up, pushed along the ceiling by the flow of air behind it, cooled on its journey as its heat is radiated and conducted to cooler ceiling and walls, and eventually contracts and sinks floorward, to rush like a moth toward the area of lesser pressure near the stove.

Riding high for a slow fall

In the atmosphere, this cycle occurs on a mighty scale, and in a far from simple fashion, between the earth's equatorial regions and the frigid areas of the poles. Air is hot around the bulging center of the earth—the place where the most solar energy strikes, the place where the most heat is trapped by water vapor, the place where a description of weather must begin. The air expands, is pushed up and spreads northward or southward. Far below, cold air travels toward the equator to take its place. The body of warm air, perhaps five to 10 miles high, moves out into the areas of lower pressure. Cooling and sinking, it goes on a long, adventurous journey, at last coming to earth again far to the north or south. Cold, dense and dry, it starts to push its way back to the equator.

Convection moves heat from tropics to ice caps, and to countless places in between as well. Convection is the sea breeze that blows in toward the hot land by day, and the land breeze that heads out to sea at night, after the earth has radiated off much of its heat. Convection sends air blowing up a sunbaked mountain by day, and brings the cool mountain air down to the warm valley at night. On small scale or large, whether it is moving from walls to stove, from sea to land or from pole to equator, the net effect of convection is to move air from cooler places to warmer, and to transfer heat from warmer places to cooler.

Yet, simple as this circulatory principle of convection sounds, in practice it rarely works smoothly beyond the threshold of that small, stove-warmed room. Winds and landscape can turn things topsy-turvy and place dense air on top of lighter. Air pressures are far from neatly graduated north and south from the equator. The earth's rotation skews rivers of air from north and south to east and west. Differences be-

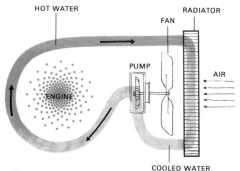

THE TRANSFER OF HEAT in the atmosphere is explained in part by this diagram of an internal-combustion engine. Most automobile engines are water-cooled. The water, pumped into a jacket surrounding the hot cylinders, absorbs the engine's heat, and is returned to the top of the radiator. It moves down through the honeycomb of metal, transferring its heat to cool air drawn through the radiator by the fan. This process is basically analogous to atmospheric circulation. Hot tropical air flows to the polar regions to be cooled. It then moves back toward the equator, where it is reheated. Without this circulation, the tropics would become unbearably hot, the poles unimaginably cold.

tween land and water, day and night, cause abrupt temperature changes. Smooth sheets of air do not flow majestically from equator to poles and back. Rather, the air is driven astray by random irregularities. Units of air are generated, collide and merge. Heat exchange takes place in brawling currents, rapids, whirlpools and eruptions of the ever-restless atmosphere.

The largest units of air are those called air masses. If a body of air hovers long enough over a large, distinctive geographical feature, like an ocean, it tends to take on the temperature and moisture characteristics of the surface below. An air mass may cover several million square miles. It can be described as a coherent mass because its temperature and moisture-content are fairly uniform at any given altitude; and once it starts to move, it moves as a body.

Air masses are among the most important moving parts of the atmospheric engine. Throughout the world there are some 20 source regions for such masses of air. Air masses heading north meet and interact with those heading south in the temperate zones, giving the latitudes of the U.S. their changeable and much-criticized weather (the weather that caused Don Marquis to remark, "Don't cuss the climate—it probably doesn't like you any better than you like it").

The U.S. is visited chiefly by three basic kinds of air masses. Maritime tropical air (designated mT on weather maps) is heated by the sun beating on tropical waters. It is crammed with latent energy, which occasionally explodes as a hurricane. Much of the warmth reaching the U.S. comes from these water-laden masses, moving north at the rate of 400 to 500 miles a day from the mid-Pacific, the Gulf of Mexico or the Caribbean Sea.

Continental polar air (cP) delivers most of America's cold. Originating over Alaska and northern Canada, it is poor in latent-heat energy, dry as well as cold, and in winter or summer brings the blue skies of good weather.

Maritime polar air (mP) originates over northern waters in the Northern Hemisphere, and has more latent energy than continental polar air. It brings North Atlantic gales to the Northeastern states, and piles snow on the west, or windward, side of the Cascade Mountains in Oregon and Washington.

Characters waiting in the wings

These are the main characters in the daily drama of temperate-zone weather. U.S. residents know them well, for they give us not only our wide contrasts of weather from north to south, from Mississippi delta to Minnesota forests, but also the essence of temperate-zone weather—mercurial change. Tropical and polar air masses meet and do battle over our heads. Often, not even the weatherman knows which one will win. The chief of the U.S. Weather Bureau made a celebrated slip in 1909, when he predicted clear weather for President Taft's inauguration and the ceremonies were caught in a howling snowstorm. His resignation did not solve the problems of the U.S. Weather Bureau. In 1916, a Congressman proposed abolishing the Bureau on the grounds that one of his constituents made better weather predictions with a sourwood stick. Unfortunately, both the constituent's name and his invaluable sourwood stick have been lost to history.

Every once in a while a northbound mass unexpectedly holds off a southbound one—or the other way around—ushering in an Indian summer in October, a thaw in February or a week of cool nights in July. The collisions and interactions of air masses generate winds, rains and thunderstorms from Cape Cod to San Francisco. Temperatures in Chicago or Butte typically shuttle over a range of 40° in any given month: they usually vary that much within a week, and often within a single day.

As Mark Twain warned, "Weather is a literary specialty, and no untrained hand can turn out a good article on it." The transfer of the world's supply of heat that produces weather is cumbersome, inefficient and turbulent. It is the bane of the weatherman; for the rest of us it is sometimes a sower of despair, and sometimes a delight.

Man against Hurricanes

The hurricane—sometimes called typhoon, willy-willy, *baguio* or tropical cyclone —is nature's most destructive force. A whirling windstorm of enormous power that is spawned mysteriously and suddenly in the otherwise gentle-weathered tropics, it goes roaring northward to wreak its capricious will across thousands of miles of sea and shore. In the Atlantic and Caribbean, about 10 hurricanes are born every year. Since 1900 they have cost the lives of 12,000 U.S. citizens and destroyed some $15 billion of U.S. property. The loss might have been less if men knew more about hurricanes—why, when and where they are formed, and why they veer in the directions they do. Weathermen are making urgent efforts to solve these puzzles, so they can give warning early enough to allow citizens to batten down or flee. One day, perhaps, man will know enough about hurricanes to stop or steer them. Until then, about all he can do is take cover.

MAN MEETING HIS MATCH
A lone man rocks off balance as a hurricane batters the waterfront at Palm Beach, Florida. When this picture was taken, winds were gusting to 100 miles an hour, with highest winds still to come. At a storm's peak, winds may hit 150 to 200 miles an hour—striking with such force that clothes are ripped from people's backs, cars swept from roads, trains brushed off their tracks.

Seeking to Know the Enemy

United States hurricane research began in a small way in the Spanish-American War, when the storms so threatened U.S. forces that President McKinley commented, "I am more afraid of a West Indian hurricane than of the entire Spanish Navy."

But no large-scale hurricane studies began until 1955, when Hurricanes Connie and Diane smashed an unprepared East Coast, costing billions of dollars in damage. After that the National Hurricane Center was set up at Miami, with the job of locating and tracking hurricanes, and, if possible, learning to predict their paths and perhaps controlling them.

Today, hurricanes are usually spotted at sea by passing ships or by one of the "hurricane-hunter" airplanes that patrol the Caribbean-Atlantic seedbed of storms. After locating the hurricane, the meteorologists make an intensive effort to chart its course and warn those in its path. Such warnings are not issued lightly; it costs Miami's Dade County about three million dollars to batten down —mainly in lost business. But an unannounced hurricane might cost a third more in property damage—and, more important, the lives of hundreds.

CLEO'S RADAR SIGNATURE
A radarscope in the Miami Weather Bureau becomes the most useful plotting instrument after the storm has approached within 250 miles of the mainland. Here the scope shows the pinwheel of 1964's Hurricane Cleo about 77 miles north of Miami (at the center of the scope).

CHARTING THE ADVANCING THREAT
A weather observer in the National Hurricane Center *(below)* plots the latest position of Hurricane Cleo, as radioed in by an Air Force airplane flying in the storm. The Navy also tracks hurricanes; the line on the map shows the division of responsibility between the two services.

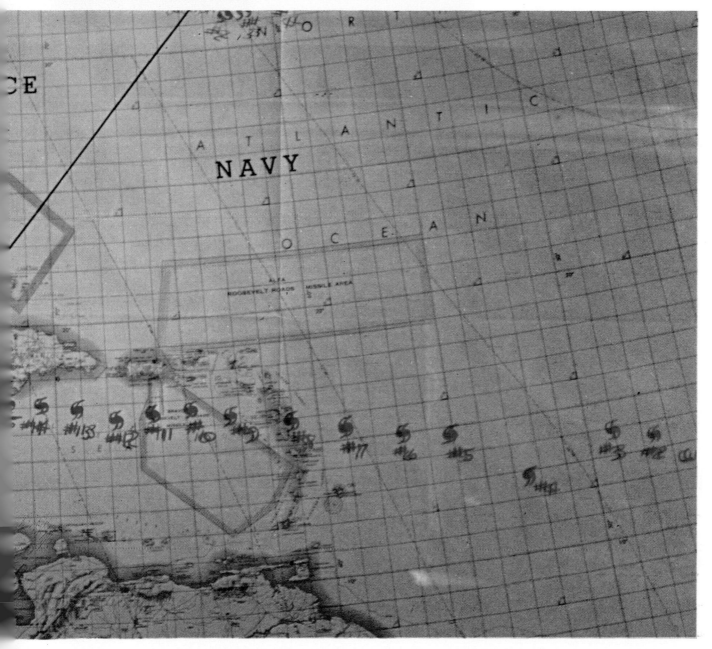

RED FLAGS OF DANGER
Red and black hurricane warning flags fly at Miami before a storm passes over the city. Although hurricane flags are still required by international maritime convention, their purpose —to warn shipping of the approaching storm— has now been largely taken over by radio.

Keeping a Weather Eye Peeled

Once a hurricane begins to bear down on the mainland, the best defense against it is information. The main data-gathering arm of the National Hurricane Center is the fleet of planes and pilots supplied by the armed forces and the Weather Bureau. After the hurricane is located, these planes make several penetrations each day into the maelstrom's heart—the quiet eye of the storm, around which whirl turbulent 100- to 200-mph winds.

These risky flights pinpoint the exact location of the storm's center and help determine its force and the various factors that will govern its path and lifetime.

With this information in hand, Hurricane Center forecasters advise threatened coastal areas to hoist hurricane flags, and issue press, radio and TV warnings. When the warnings go out, inhabitants of low-lying areas are advised to seek shelter above the highest predicted tide levels, to stock up on drinking water and foods that need no refrigeration, to store loose objects and to tape windows.

A HURRICANE HUNTER AT WORK
Engines turning over at the Miami airport, a Weather Bureau plane *(above)* prepares to take off for a research flight on a hurricane. Inside the plane *(right)* researchers record data while actually flying in the storm's eye. Banks of dials at left show temperature, humidity, pressure and winds. The seated man at right watches a radarscope that tells the shape of the storm.

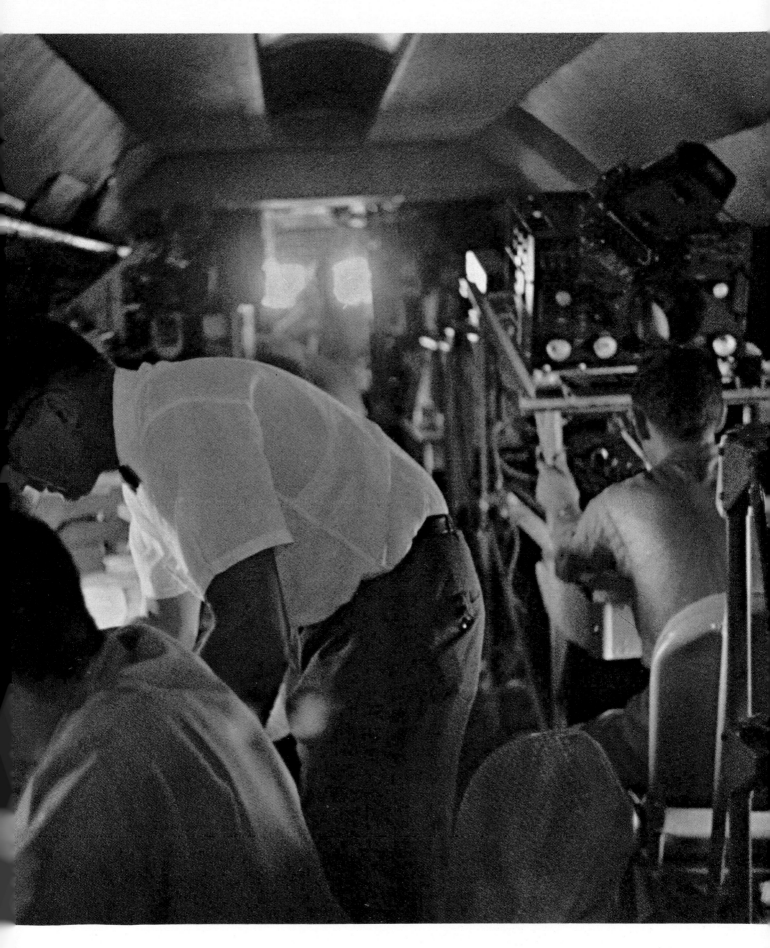

Piercing a Hurricane's Heart

Until 1943, no aircraft had ever flown into a hurricane. That year an Army Air Force colonel, Joseph P. Duckworth, piloted a single-engine trainer into a hurricane's eye. "The only embarrassing episode," he later commented in his report, "would have been engine failure, which, with the strong ground winds, would probably have prevented a landing, and certainly would have made descent via parachute highly inconvenient." Since then more vicious hurricanes than Duckworth's have severely damaged hurricane-hunter aircraft, and one such plane was never heard from after it entered a storm.

Once a plane ventures into a hurricane it endures a few minutes of pounding winds and waterfall rain—and then it enters the eye. Like a sheltered lagoon, the eye is devoid of all the terrors of the surrounding wall of clouds. The sun or stars may be out and gentle breezes may be blowing. But there is no way of leaving this peaceful haven without meeting the storm's full fury once more.

A MAELSTROM'S PEACEFUL INTERIOR
A hurricane's eye looks like this from an altitude of 18,000 feet with blue sea visible below through broken clouds. The swirls at left are clouds torn from the wall of the eye and swept into the center, where gentle winds prevail.

New Help from Science

Meteorologists do not yet have a scientific theory that permits them to predict the paths of hurricanes with real accuracy. But several recent scientific advances offer hope. First, the weather satellites Tiros and Nimbus permit a reduction in the number of airplane flights being made to find hurricanes. In addition, electronic computers are helping forecasters juggle the immense quantity of data that must be considered when trying to decide where a hurricane will go next.

Finally, since 1961 a special U.S. Weather Bureau program called Project Stormfury has been investigating methods for reducing the hurricane's force. Most of Stormfury's hope is placed in the chemical, silver iodide. Crystals of this material dropped into hurricane clouds can sometimes cause the cloud moisture to freeze. It is hoped that this technique, when perfected, may interrupt the flow of air currents in and out of the storm sufficiently to break up the hurricane.

INTELLIGENCE CENTER AT WORK

During a storm, Miami hurricane specialists *(opposite)* use space-age information to keep the public informed. Xavier Proenza *(foreground)* pieces together satellite photographs to make a composite hurricane picture; forecaster Ray Kraft pores over a map before issuing warnings.

WEATHER SPY IN THE SKY

A Nimbus I experimental weather satellite *(above)* rides out to orbit from California atop a Thor Agena booster. During its lifetime of less than a month, the first Nimbus photographed the 1964 hurricanes Cleo, Dora, Ethel and Florence, plus Pacific typhoons Ruby and Sally.

SPACE PORTRAIT OF A STORM

This Nimbus photograph *(right)*, with an outline map of Florida superimposed, one of a sequence of frames that were taken August 29, 1964, shows Hurricane Cleo. Less than four minutes after Nimbus pictures are taken, they can be viewed by ground-based weathermen.

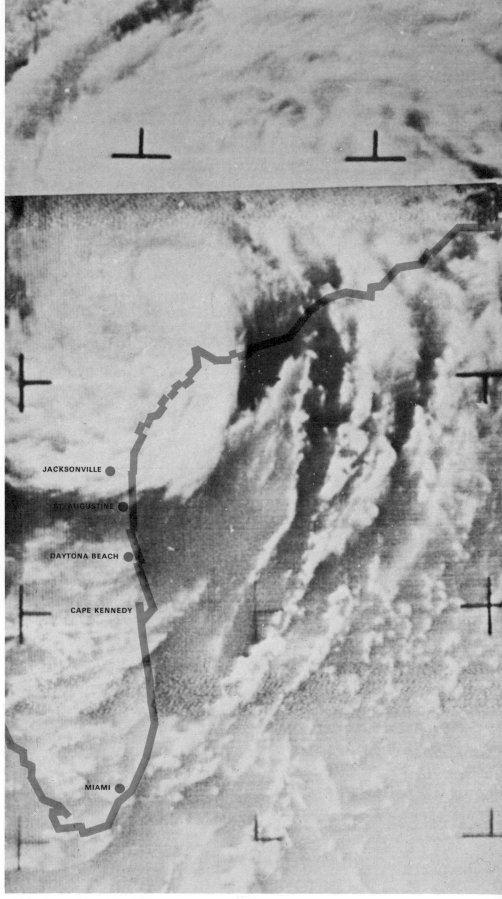

JACKSONVILLE

ST. AUGUSTINE

DAYTONA BEACH

CAPE KENNEDY

MIAMI

INTERMEDIATE CLOUD DECK

RAI

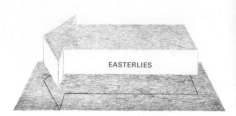

EASTERLIES

(1) THE STORM'S PARENT WIND

The four diagrams here and below illustrate one widely accepted theory of the birth and decay of a typical Atlantic hurricane. The arrow above represents the steady flow of the easterlies, or trade winds, as they blow in late summer over seas having a temperature of at least 80° F.

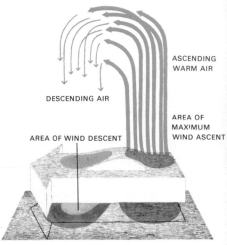

ASCENDING WARM AIR

DESCENDING AIR

AREA OF MAXIMUM WIND ASCENT

AREA OF WIND DESCENT

(2) A LIFT TO THE UPPER AIR

The first step in the birth of a hurricane usually occurs when a low-pressure disturbance diverts part of the easterly northward. The winds, squeezed at this curve, pile up on one another. Their warm air rises as high as 40,000 feet, releasing heat and moisture before descending.

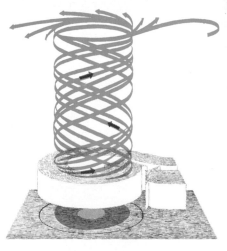

(3) PICKING UP MOMENTUM

The rotation of the earth imparts a twist to the rising column, which gradually takes the form of a cylinder whirling around a core of relatively still air. Warm, moist air drawn in off the sea picks up speed as it comes, constantly feeding energy to the rising, whirling column of winds.

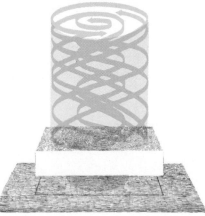

EYE FILLING UP

A HURRICANE'S ARCHITECTURE

A cross section of a hurricane (height greatly exaggerated) shows the cloudless eye, around which spiral ascending winds. The secondary cloud deck is an exit path for some of the rising air. Most of the heavy rain falls from rainbands that spiral in toward the storm's center.

(4) DYING OF STARVATION

The last stage in a hurricane's life begins when it moves over land or colder water. Without warm, damp air the storm loses its energy. The cooler air cannot climb so high. The winds drop off, gradually the eye fills in with clouds, and the hurricane expands in area and dissipates.

52

PATH OF WIND FLOW

EYE

AREA OF
MINIMUM
PRESSURE

The Structure of a Giant Storm

Few people suffering under the hurricane's bewildering lash would suspect that the chaos and confusion going on all around them is really part of a well-defined structure that hurricanes have in common.

One important feature is the rainbands that spiral into the center. Until the development of radar, men were unaware that rainbands existed. Now they are the principal way of identifying a hurricane on a radarscope or satellite picture.

These rainbands indicate the paths of winds bringing in the storm's essential diet of warm, moist air that feeds into the central "wall clouds."

Meteorologists still do not fully understand all the conditions necessary to produce a hurricane. In particular they are mystified by the way many events interact to trigger a self-sustaining hurricane (diagrams at left). What they do know about the relative frequency with which hurricane-inducing conditions occur leads them to puzzle over another problem: why don't hurricanes occur more often?

In the Path of Destruction

Between 1955 and 1964, U.S. hurricanes caused more than 1,000 deaths and property damage estimated at more than $10 billion.

Much of this damage occurred in the Northeast, once considered virtually immune to the big windstorms. For years the Gulf States bore the brunt of the hurricanes' fury. In one 1900 storm, 6,000 lives were lost in Galveston. Then, in 1938, the Northeast was hit by its first major hurricane since 1869, heralding a shift of most hurricane paths eastward. Most climatologists believe that a warming trend in the '30s caused the shift. Now some predict that hurricane paths will move into the Gulf States again. But the only thing that can be said with certainty is that wherever the hurricane's trail goes, it will be paved with grief and destruction.

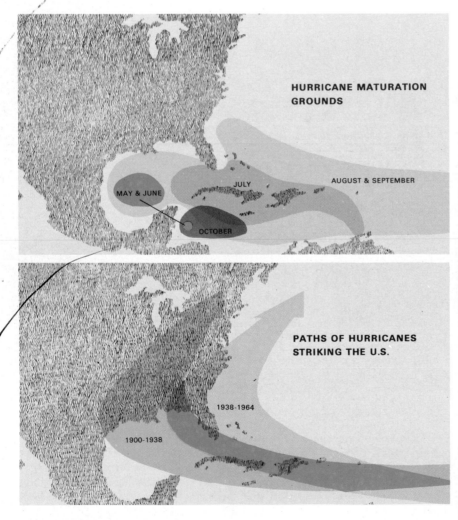

HURRICANE MATURATION GROUNDS

MAY & JUNE

JULY

AUGUST & SEPTEMBER

OCTOBER

PATHS OF HURRICANES STRIKING THE U.S.

1938-1964

1900-1938

CHANGING TRENDS IN STORMS

Of the two maps above, the lower one indicates the general eastward shift of the hurricanes that struck the continent of North America from 1900 to 1964. The top one shows the areas where tropical storms tend to build to hurricane intensity at different times of the year.

In May and June, hurricanes come from the western Caribbean and the Gulf of Mexico. By July they are mainly coming from the Lesser Antilles northward. Fall hurricanes are well scattered, but by October there remains one small area of concentration in the western Caribbean.

A Jacksonville couple poke in the ruins of their house, leveled by pounding seas and wind.

3
Winds of the World

To the ordinary man, wind may be many things—a balm or a scourge, an annoyance or a blessing. But to the meteorologist, it is air in motion. As such, it is energy. It streams in silent rivers across the sky, surges in invisible cataracts over mountain ridges, boils heavenward over hot deserts and humid rain forests, swirls in furious, catastrophic maelstroms over Kansas, and the Caribbean and China Seas. It is power of cosmic magnitude. Scientists have estimated that if all the earth's atmosphere were moving at a leisurely 20 miles per hour—the speed of a light breeze—its energy at any one moment would equal the energy generated by the Hoover Dam operating at full capacity, night and day, for 6,680 years.

The wind energy performs prodigious tasks—tasks essential to the maintenance of the atmosphere's activities. It fills the sky with clouds, then sweeps it clear again. It drives the cooling, moisture-laden fogs in off the sea. It blows entire storm systems halfway around the world, moving heat and moisture from one region of the earth to another. It air-conditions and ventilates cities that lie along great bodies of water, like San Francisco and Chicago. It helps to push the ocean currents on their global journeys. It sculptures sand and snow, scatters seeds and spores. It clears the heavens of the poisonous exhalations of our machines and factories.

What makes the wind blow? And why does it blow first this way, then that—now weak, now strong? The answer is, uneven atmospheric pressure. Because there are always differences in the temperature of the atmosphere, there are also pressure differences, and these differences naturally seek to balance themselves. High-pressure air in a child's balloon, when released, rushes outward to join low-pressure air. Air under 30 pounds of pressure in a tire may, if the tire has a weak spot, burst through to meet the average 14.7-pound pressure of the surrounding atmosphere. Similarly, wind movement is caused by the forces acting to push air from higher to lower pressure.

Men always guessed—and later knew—that the wind carried messages about future weather. Wind out of one quarter meant fair weather, wind out of another, storms. And so they watched the way trees bent, the way smoke drifted. They wet a finger and held it up; the cool side faced the wind. In ancient times, as today, the wind was named for the direction *from* which it blew. "Out of the south cometh the whirlwind," says the Book of Job. But steady south winds also brought hot weather to Biblical lands. "When ye see the south wind blow, ye say, There will be heat; and it cometh to pass," wrote St. Luke. Bartholomaeus Anglicus, a 13th Century scholar, noted that "The North winde . . . purgeth and cleanseth raine, and driveth away clowdes and mistes, and bringeth in cleereness and faire wether; and againward, for the South winde is hot

BUFFETED BY BREEZES
A caped stroller loses his hat and his composure as he struggles into the wind in this 19th Century caricature titled "March Wind." Meteorologically, the traditionally brisk winds of March are explained by exaggerated temperature differences that exist between the north polar region and the equator about the time of the vernal equinox, during the early spring.

& moyst, it doth the contrary deedes: for it maketh the aire thicke and troubly, & breedeth darknesse."

Today the methods of linking wind and weather are somewhat more complicated. Forecasters want to know first what the barometer is doing, and only then which way the wind is blowing. Once these facts are in hand, however, their matter-of-fact prose bears out the findings of the ancients. "When the wind sets in from points between south and southeast and the barometer falls steadily," reads the U.S. Weather Bureau's *Weather Forecasting* (1963 edition), "a storm is approaching from the west or northwest, and its center will pass near or north of the observer within 12 to 24 hours, with the wind shifting to northwest by way of south and southwest...."

Shuttlecocks and cloud shadows

The wind's usefulness as an aid to weather forecasting led men to devise all sorts of systems and gadgets for studying it. Primitive weathermen of China and Egypt built wind vanes that showed the directions from which the wind was blowing. In 17th Century Europe, in the earliest days of modern meteorology, scientists measured the speed and force of wind by setting feathers adrift in it and watching their passage between two points. Or they measured the speed at which the wind blew a feathered cork disk along a wire. Sometimes they clocked the velocity of cloud shadows across a stretch of water or an open field.

In the 1760s, in Danzig, Michael Christoph Hanov tried to standardize wind-force measurements by raising flags of various lengths and noting at a given moment which one the wind lifted to a horizontal position. Hanov also experimented with a single flag loaded with varying weights; he based one of his wind-force tables on still another scale —the degree of movement of a length of lead-weighted horsehair.

By the mid-19th Century scientists were measuring the velocity of the wind by noting the rate at which it evaporated or cooled water. And one experimenter—presumably with perfect pitch—even used a device resembling wind chimes, rating the wind's speed according to the musical sounds it produced. About the same period, science hit upon the instrument that, in improved form, is still widely used today to measure wind velocity: the cup anemometer. A modern anemometer consists of three or four cups mounted at the end of horizontal arms that extend at right angles from a vertical shaft. The wind catches the cups, spins them around and rotates the shaft. The shaft is geared to a device that, like an automobile speedometer, registers the rate of revolution in terms of miles per hour.

But the complicated methods of modern forecasting require vast amounts of information—far more than the ground-level data that wind

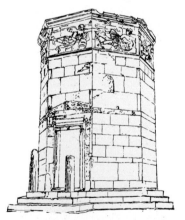

AN EARLY OBSERVATORY, this Athenian "Tower of the Winds" dates to the First Century B.C. On its eight faces are carved figures representing the eight winds recognized by Aristotle three centuries earlier, four of which are reproduced at right. Aristotle seems to have anticipated modern ideas of polar fronts as determinants of weather: he divided winds into two classes, polar and equatorial, and described with amazing accuracy the weather likely to be brought by each.

BOREAS, OR NORTH WIND

NOTOS, OR SOUTH WIND

vanes and anemometers supply. In the Western Hemisphere alone, 145 U.S. Weather Bureau stations send up more than 600,000 balloons a year to gather information on the upper atmosphere. At least 120,000 of them are sounding balloons, from each of which dangles a tiny electronic device called a radiosonde (*sonde* is French for "sounding line"). The radiosonde combines meteorological sensing equipment with a radio transmitter. As the balloon drifts aloft, rising at about 1,000 feet a minute, it sends back continuous reports on temperature, pressure and humidity until it rises to somewhere between 75,000 and 125,000 feet—where it bursts. Sometimes, additional information is supplied by electronic direction-finders on the ground, which gather data on wind speed and direction by following the same balloon's path and speed by radar.

Weather balloons sometimes carry aloft special metal-foil reflectors that are tracked by ground-based radar. These balloons are called rawinsondes (rawin is an acronym for *ra*dar and *win*d). On clear days ground observers watch the course of bright-colored pilot balloons, tracking wind speed and direction visually. Also, the Weather Bureau, NASA, the Department of Defense and the Air Force all use rockets of various kinds to collect weather data. Some eject chemicals and bundles of metal strips, which are tracked by camera and radar; others are equipped with grenades that explode in the upper air, generating sound waves that yield data on high-altitude winds.

These investigations and others like them—made possible primarily as a result of the technological developments since World War II—have confirmed some heretofore unprovable theories, answered some once-unanswerable questions and settled some old arguments. They have also cast doubt upon some long-accepted points of view, a few of them quite basic. Nevertheless, much is known about the winds—how they are formed, and how and why they blow.

To begin with, winds are grouped into three categories: local and regional persistent winds; global persistent winds; and maverick, or episodic, winds, like cyclones and anticyclones, tornadoes and hurricanes.

Winds of sea and land, hill and valley

Local, persistent winds are almost invariably small-scale convection winds—the sea breeze and the land breeze, the mountain wind and the valley wind. Because they are comparatively shallow in depth and limited in range, they are simple winds. They blow from high-pressure area to low-pressure area, practically unaffected by such complicating factors as the rotation of the earth.

The sea breeze and the land breeze are caused by the difference in the temperature of the air over the land and water. During the day, the sun warms the land, and the land warms the air above it. The air rises—

APELIOTES. OR EAST WIND

ZEPHYROS. OR WEST WIND

and cool, heavier air flows in off the sea to take its place. During the night, the process is reversed: the sea, retaining much of its daytime warmth, warms the air over it—which rises and is replaced by heavier, cooler air blowing off the land.

The sea breeze and its nocturnal opposite appear with virtually clock-like regularity along the coastlines of the tropics and subtropics. It is an old, dependable and blessed friend, bearing picturesque, poetic names: the *virazón* of Chile, the *datoo* of Gibraltar, the *imbat* of Morocco, the *ponente* of Italy, the *kapalilua* of Hawaii, the "doctor" of various English-speaking tropical and semitropical regions. Further north, the sea breeze tends to be seasonal, appearing in the warmer weather of late spring and summer, especially during June and July. The seasonal sea breeze habitually springs up between 10 and 11 o'clock in the morning, and starts to subside at about 2 o'clock in the afternoon. By 7 or 8 o'clock at night it has died out altogether. Then the land breeze begins to freshen, and the time sequence is repeated.

The hotter the climate, the faster and farther these breezes move, and the greater their mass. They always reach their maximum speed at the hottest time of day. In the temperate zones this top speed is a mild eight to 12 miles per hour; in the tropics it is a brisk 20 to 24 miles per hour. Their inland range in temperate zones is a mere nine or 10 miles, and their ceiling averages about 600 to 700 feet. But in the tropics the sea breeze extends 100 miles inland, and can have a ceiling of 4,000 feet or more.

Mountains as wind-makers

Mountain dwellers the world over are familiar with small-scale convection winds of a similar nature. Meteorologists call them thermal slope winds. They consist of air that blows upward (from valley floor to mountain ridge) during the warm daylight hours, and downward (off the ridges to the valley floor) during the cool hours of night. In the daytime the rocky mountainsides heat up quickly and generate rising currents of air. It is considerably warmer than the air at the same altitude over the valley. The cooler, heavier air over the valley presses down, and in effect squeezes the air up the slopes—where it becomes heated and joins the circulation system. Soon after sunset, the mountainside cools swiftly—much more swiftly than the valley. Then warm air rises vertically over the valley, while heavier cold air flows down the slopes —and the circulation system is reversed.

In long, deep valleys—like those of the High Sierras or Alps—the valley wind, in addition to traveling up the sloping sides of the mountains, also flows up the long axis of the valley, from its wide to its narrow end. Frequently hot and unremitting, it raises choking clouds of dust from

RIDING THE WARM AIR, a glider traversing open country uses the natural vertical motion of thermal or convective currents to remain in flight. The steep slope of air thrown up by a coastal ridge *(left)* enables the glider to gain altitude. Warm air rising over a city boosts it higher. It then dips toward earth in the downdraft of cooler air above a forest, soars again in thermal updrafts over a plowed field, and finally descends in the downdraft over a pond. Meanwhile a second glider *(right)* is descending from a great height in the layered waves that form in the lee of a mountain range.

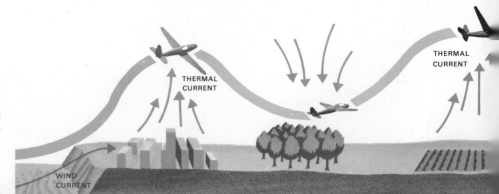

THERMAL CURRENT

THERMAL CURRENT

WIND CURRENT

the valley floor and blows so steadily, year in and year out, that it deforms trees in its path. It denudes them of branches on the windward side, and twists their leeward branches into frozen free-form shapes. After sunset this valley wind subsides, and is replaced by a cooler, lighter breeze from the slopes and peaks at the valley's ends.

All over the world there are persistent small-scale winds that derive their unique character from local topography—the so-called orographic winds. One kind of orographic wind is the trans-mountain wind—like the *chinook*, the *föhn*, and the *zonda*, all of which will be described later. Trans-mountain winds lose their moisture as they ascend the mountain barrier, then blow warm and parching down the leeward slopes into the valley beyond. Another common orographic wind is the bora, frequently referred to as a fall wind or drainage wind, because it is a wide, massive river of air that falls or drains from high, cold plateau country onto a warm plain or coastal region.

Unlike the warm trans-mountain winds, the bora blows across the land cold and furious, under bitter-bright and sunny skies. It is named for the most celebrated local wind of its type, the bora that howls down out of the Balkans and at times all but paralyzes the Adriatic littoral from Trieste to the border of Albania. The prototype bora begins in Russia, crosses the high Hungarian plains, then the north-south ridge of the Julian and Dinaric Alps. Beyond the Alps, it falls down the mountains' seaward slopes to the Dalmatian plain, then blows out across the Adriatic Sea, where it whips up waves, atomizing their crests into a spindrift mist that Italian mariners call *fumarea*.

The wind that overturns rocks

The famous French mistral is a boralike wind that drains off the plateau of central France. Cold, dry, bleak and relentless, it blows south from Burgundy in the spring and autumn, funnels down the narrow corridor of the Rhone Valley, then sweeps across Provence to the Gulf of Lions. "An impetuous and terrible wind," wrote the Greek geographer Strabo in the First Century A.D., "which displaces rocks, hurls men from their chariots, crushes their limbs, and strips them of their clothes and arms. . . ."

Two thousand years have failed to mellow the mistral. To this day, it can still blow a man off a horse, upset a carload of hay and shatter windows with a blast of pebbles. In Arles, the mistral once nudged loose a string of engineless freight cars and blew them 25 miles to Port-St.-Louis before trainmen could board them and brake them to a stop.

But the most dramatic—and historic—of the regional, persistent winds is the monsoon, a word derived from the Arabic *mausim*, or "season." It was first applied to the seasonal winds of the Arabian Sea that blow

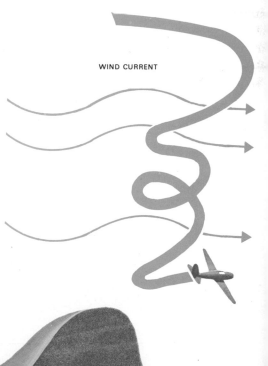

WIND CURRENT

six months from the northeast, then reverse and blow just as steadily six months from the southwest. The monsoon has always played an important role in the economy of the Middle and Far East. It blew the frail craft of the first adventurous traders from the east coast of Africa across the Indian Ocean to the rich Malabar Coast of India. And in the First Century A.D., Arabian mariners, trimming their sails to it, fared safely northeast across the Gulf of Aden to the mouth of the Indus River. Three centuries later, they rode the steady monsoon winds all the way to China. Even today, India's economy is at the mercy of the monsoon. The country's huge rice crop, the staple food for its teeming millions, depends on moisture that the monsoon brings from the Indian Ocean.

A vast sea breeze

In simplest terms, the monsoon is a sea and land breeze, writ large. Instead of being limited to narrow strips of coastline, it sweeps back and forth over hundreds of thousands of square miles of land and sea. And instead of being set to the rhythm of day and night, it is keyed to the cycle of summer and winter. The land heats in summer and cools in winter, but the temperature of adjacent ocean areas remains relatively constant. As a result, massive convective updrafts rise over the land in summer, and air travels inland off the ocean to take its place—creating the long, moisture-laden summer monsoon. During the winter, when the continents are cooler than the oceans, the process is reversed.

Monsoonlike winds exist in many parts of the world, but the best defined monsoons are two Asiatic systems divided by the Himalayas. One is the East Asia monsoon, the predominant wind of Japan and mainland China. The other is the South Asia monsoon, powered by heating and cooling of the great Indian peninsula jutting into the Indian Ocean.

Mechanically, the trade winds that blow over the great ocean areas of the tropics and subtropics are like the monsoons. They are large-scale convection winds that blow predictably and persistently. But the range of the trade winds is global rather than regional, and they blow always in the same direction. They are planetary wind systems, and they form part of what meteorologists call the "general circulation" of the atmosphere—the three great bands of wind that blow around the globe in the Northern and Southern Hemispheres.

Like all convective systems, the general circulation is powered by an imbalance in temperature—in this case a difference between the temperature at the two poles and the equator. Warm equatorial air rises and flows generally poleward, cold polar air sinks and flows generally toward the equator. But several factors complicate this simple concept of two hemispheric loops, or "conveyor belts," of moving air. One is the drag of the air against the earth's surface, the other is the rotation of the earth itself. Together, friction and rotation combine to throw the general circulation into an enormous, swirling concatenation of currents.

In tracing the course of these currents the logical place to begin is at the equator. A theoretical line called the heat equator girdles the globe through its hottest points. On both sides of this shifting line lies the region known since sailing-ship days as the doldrums, but which meteorologists call the "inter-tropical convergence zone." The air over the doldrums has very little horizontal movement—the sun's blazing heat lifts it almost straight up. This rising air branches outward like a fountain, some of it turning north, some of it south, to form the upper-level air currents known as the antitrade winds. As they reach 25° latitude, north and south, the antitrades also divide. One stream, continuing toward the poles, forms the upper level of the winds known as the westerlies. The other begins to descend back to earth, where it piles up in the region of the 30th parallel, creating a fair-weather zone of calm air. Sailors call this zone the "horse latitudes," perhaps because of the horses that died and had to be thrown overboard when Spanish ships heading for the Indies were becalmed here for weeks at a time.

When the descending air of the horse latitudes reaches the earth, it too divides, one stream returning to the equator, the other heading toward the poles. The equatorial current forms the famous trade winds—the mild, gentle winds that blew Columbus to America, the steadiest, most persistent winds on earth. This, indeed, is how they earned their name. "Trade" is an ancient word for track or path, and to "blow trade" is to blow steadily and incessantly in the same direction, along the same track. The trade winds replace the air rising over the doldrums, thus completing the equatorial convection system—a system generally referred to by meteorologists as the "Hadley cell," after George Hadley, who first suggested its existence in the 18th Century.

The effect of the spinning earth

If the earth were stationary, the trade winds would blow directly from north to south in the Northern Hemisphere, and the opposite way in the Southern Hemisphere. But the spin of the earth, west to east, deflects or steers the trades—and in fact all winds of the general circulation—making them veer off their strictly north-south course. This effect is called the Coriolis force (although it is not, strictly speaking, a real force at all). It takes its name from the 19th Century French mathematician, Gaspard Gustave de Coriolis, who first described it.

The air currents moving toward the poles from the horse latitudes are deflected eastward and merge into the prevailing westerlies—the second of the great wind systems of the general circulation. The westerlies circle the earth in waving skeins between the 30th and 60th parallels. Em-

ABETTING SLAVERY, the trade winds and the prevailing westerlies, indicated on the map below by colored arrows, helped make the traffic in Negroes possible from the 16th to the late 19th Century. A ship such as the one shown above voyaged on the northeast trades from Europe to Africa with goods to be exchanged for slaves. Loaded with human cargo, she would ride the trade winds to the Americas, there to barter slaves for sugar, rum or cotton. Then she would return to Europe on the prevailing westerlies to renew the cycle.

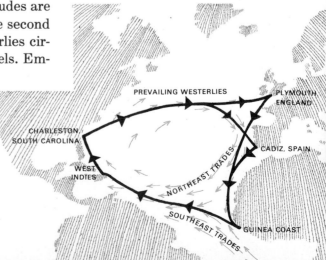

bedded in their main currents, roughly six miles out, are the jet streams that, blowing at an average of 200 to 300 miles an hour, push eastbound airliners across the American continent two hours faster than they can make the same flight in the opposite direction.

The wildest winds

Even at ground level the westerlies can be the wildest of all the persistent winds. In the Southern Hemisphere they rush unimpeded, at gale force, across thousands of miles of open water, driving before them scudding storm clouds and rolling the sea into mountainous waves 60 feet high. Awestruck sailors encounter them most frequently in the latitudes between 40° and 50° south, and call the region the "roaring forties." But as they near the poles, the westerlies lose their speed and force—much as the water at the banks of a stream loses its forward motion and drifts into eddying backwaters. At the 60th parallel they brush against the last of the bands of winds that make up the general circulation—the polar easterlies.

The polar easterlies begin as masses of cold air bred by conditions on the earth's surface. Just as there is a heat equator circling the earth through its hottest points, coinciding roughly with the geographical equator, so there are poles of intense cold in the vicinity of the geographical North and South Poles. In the Northern Hemisphere one of these poles of cold is in Siberia, and includes the two towns of Verkhoyansk and Oymyakon, where temperatures have reportedly reached −90° F. Another lies in northwestern Canada, where the town of Snag has reported a low of −81° F. A third cold pole in the Northern Hemisphere is in Greenland. In the Southern Hemisphere the great pole of cold is on the continent of Antarctica, where a Soviet weather station, Vostok, has registered a temperature of −126.9° F. These poles of cold breed far-spreading mantles of heavy, frigid air that fan out and move toward the equator, are deflected by the Coriolis force, and are the polar easterlies.

Most of the northern temperate zone's changeable weather originates along the undulating line where the polar easterlies and prevailing westerlies meet. The clash of the two currents, with their different temperatures and humidities, creates a more or less permanent condition of atmospheric instability and perturbation; great eddies and vortices form sporadically, to move off as isolated masses of whirling wind within the general circulation. Unlike the general circulation, however, these wind systems rise and subside, are born and die—in short, are episodic. To meteorologists they are known as cyclones and anticyclones, and one is a mirror image of the other. Cyclonic wind systems spin around a center of low pressure and converge upon that center, rotating counterclockwise in the Northern Hemisphere, clockwise in the Southern Hemisphere. Anticyclonic winds rotate in the reverse direction, around a high-pressure center, and flare out from the center. But both systems are alike in one respect: they cover areas of hundreds of thousands of square miles.

Cyclones are the familiar "lows" of the weather map, the bringers of bad weather—clouds, rainstorms, blizzards. But they are not synonymous with the violent windstorms so often and mistakenly associated with their name: tornadoes are not cyclones. Anticyclones are the weather map's "highs," and normally bring good weather. Together, highs and lows account for the temperate zone's variable day-to-day weather. Moving around the globe west to east, in endless and erratic procession, they bring clear skies and searing droughts, gentle rains and tempestuous 50-mile-an-hour gales.

In the tropics a low can grow into the churning aerial maelstrom of a typhoon or hurricane—two names for the same kind of storm. Both are born over warm tropical seas, where the air is laden with moisture and heavily charged with latent heat energy. Their breeding grounds exist in half a dozen places around the world—in the northern Atlantic and Pacific Oceans, the Indian Ocean, the China and Arabian Seas. The hurricane, from *huracan*, the West Indian god of storms, sweeps in from the Atlantic about 10 times a year, roughly between the months of May and September. The typhoon, which generally makes its appearance in August and September but can occur in any season, blows up on an average of 20 times a year in the North Pacific alone. During their violent lives (described in detail in the picture essay preceding this chapter) these tropical storms do incredible damage.

Most vicious and capricious of all storms, however, is the tornado, a traveling whirlwind whose name comes from the Spanish *tronada*, thunderstorm.

The twisters of the U.S.

Tornadoes occur in many parts of the world, but nowhere do they occur with more frequency and violence than in the United States, where each year 500 to 600 of them rip their way across the countryside. Most of them occur during the afternoon, shortly after the passing of the day's highest heat, and they are always associated with thunderstorms. Green lightning flickers weirdly over the land, and dark clouds glow strangely green and yellow. They are accompanied by a sullen, remote rumble which sounds at close range like the roar of a thousand express trains traveling at top speed.

The average tornado has a central core perhaps 250 yards in diameter and may travel along the ground only 100 feet, but can go 100 miles. It usually appears as a funnel-shaped cloud, but sometimes it is a relatively

THE WRATH OF A HURRICANE was dramatically evoked in the 18th Century by an officer of the frigate H.M.S. *Egmont,* who sketched her wallowing helplessly in the Caribbean during the Great Hurricane of 1780. This storm, which was reported to London *(below)* by the governor of Jamaica, was only one of hundreds to hit the West Indies. But it was one of the worst: more than 9,000 persons were killed on Martinique alone.

A

GENERAL ACCOUNT, &c.

SECTION I.

ACCOUNTS from JAMAICA.

Copy of a Letter from Major General Dalling, Governor of the Island of Jamaica, to Lord George Germain, one of his Majesty's Principal Secretaries of State, received by his Majesty's Sloop Alert, Captain Vashon, and published in the London Gazette, Jan. 12, 1781.

My Lord,   *Jamaica, Oct.* 20, 1780.

I AM sorry to be under the disagreeable necessity of informing your Lordship of one of the most dreadful calamities that has happened to this colony within the memory of the oldest inhabitant.

On Monday the 2d instant, the weather being very close, the sky on a sudden became very much overcast, and an uncommon elevation of the sea immediately followed. Whilst the unhappy settlers at Savanna la Mar were observing this extraordinary nary straight-sided cylinder, a thin, curiously twisted rope or an elephant's trunk swinging across the eerily lit countryside.

As the tornado advances it scoops up and spews out timbers, trees, livestock, rocks, refrigerators, rooftops, cars, chickens. Even people have been carried aloft by tornadoes. In Texas, in 1947, two men were carried 200 feet by a tornado and were then set down virtually uninjured. During another tornado, a man and wife in Ponca City, Oklahoma, were inside their house when it was blown away; its walls and roof exploded, but the floor remained intact and eventually glided back to earth, depositing the couple unharmed.

The top speed of a tornado's whirlwind has never been measured; the instruments never survive. Meteorologists think it probably reaches about 400 miles an hour, and may go as high as 600 or 700 miles an hour —approaching the speed of sound. In its wake it leaves some weird testaments to its power. One tornado in 1925 drove a large plank into the trunk of a tree, wedging it firmly enough to support the weight of a man on its free end. And tornadoes regularly denude chickens of their feathers—usually, but not always, doing in the chickens as well. Terrifying and unforgettable—and intrinsically baffling—the tornado is the briefest but most intense of all the many kinds of winds that swirl in endless convolutions above the surface of the earth.

Great Rivers of Air

Tempest, zephyr, gale, breeze, squall—these are but a few of the thousand names for wind. And though man has used and been abused by winds for the 60,000 years of his existence, it has been only within this century that he has even begun to understand their behavior. Winds are the atmosphere in motion. They start to blow when warm air, expanding, is forced up, and cooled air, contracting, sinks. From this simple beginning the behavior of the winds grows almost inconceivably complex. Tropical air heads toward the poles, polar air toward the equator. The spinning of the earth makes the winds swerve, and the earth's pockmarked, irregular surface—not to mention the changing temperatures of its oceans and continents—exerts a further profound influence. Despite all this, the global winds are not chaotic. Instead, they move in stately, measured patterns, within which the most violent hurricane is little more than a momentary eddy.

FULL SAIL BEFORE THE WIND
Spinnaker bellying and trade winds aft, the 75-foot schooner *Constellation* makes good time toward Honolulu to win in its class in the 1959 Transpacific race from Los Angeles. The 2,225- mile voyage took the *Constellation* 10 days, 23 hours. Speed in such races depends largely upon expert knowledge and the utmost use of the prevailing winds that are found in tropical latitudes.

Circuits That Distribute Heat

The global movement of winds can be visualized in simplified form as a series of rotating cells, or belts *(opposite)*, propelled by differences in their temperatures. On either side of the equator, hot tropic air rises, spills outward, cools somewhat, and then sinks earthward in the vicinity of the 30th parallel of latitude. Similarly, at the poles, cold air sinks, gathers warmth, then rises again to repeat the cycle. Between each set of these thermally generated cells is a middle-latitude cell. The wind circulation in this cell, caught between the upward thrust of the polar cell on the one side and the downward pull of tropic air on the other, operates in reverse, as if it were part of a gear train. Contrary to the normal thermal movement, its warm air sinks and its cold air rises.

The total effect is as if a gigantic bucket brigade were employed in the transfer of heat away from the tropics and toward the poles. Thus a portion of the heat from each tropic cell is passed on to the mid-latitude cell; when these warmed winds reach a latitude of about 60°, they join with the rising currents of the polar cells, to which they pass along a measure of their heat.

The process is much less simple in actual operation than in the diagram: many other influences also act on the winds, turning and churning them as shown on the pages that follow.

CIRCULATION'S BOLD DESIGN
Dyed water illustrates a basic process governing air circulation. The blue water, cooled by a pipe *(right),* sinks and flows left along the bottom of the tank. Red dye, which is dropped into warmer water, first sinks of its own weight, then slowly rises to flow along the surface.

WINDS ON A FEATURELESS EARTH
Atmospheric circulation is shown below as it would occur if it were not affected by the earth's spin, tilt or topography. In this hypothetical situation, air warmed in the tropics is forced up and spreads north or south, eventually reaching the poles. Cold air from the poles flows at lower altitudes back toward the equator. If such simple circumstances actually existed, air circulation for the entire globe would follow a fixed pattern, involving two huge wind cells moving in much the same manner as the water shown in the tank at left above. Each day's weather would be the same, with the entire earth under the influence of gentle equator-bound winds.

SUN

EARTH

A GLOBAL GEAR TRAIN OPERATED BY THE TRANSFER OF HEAT

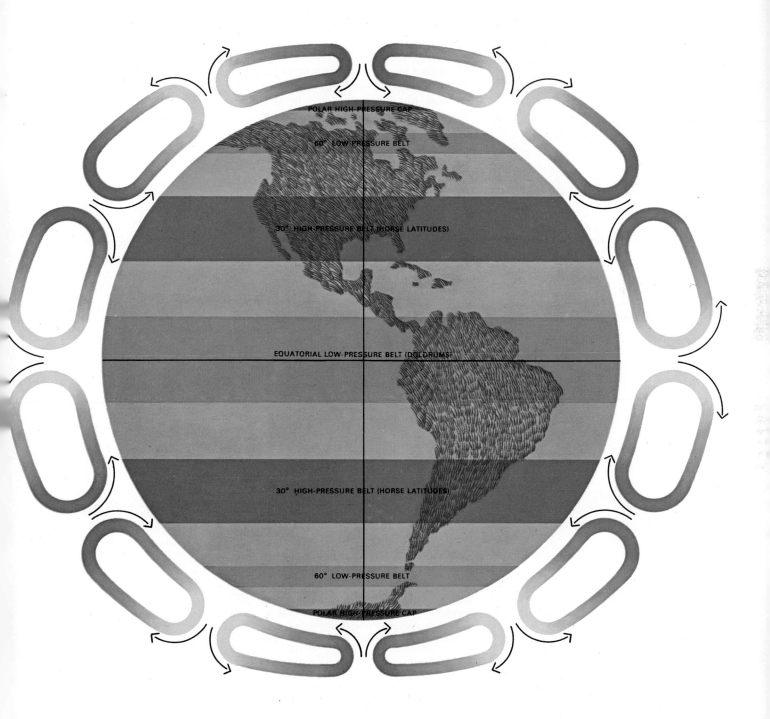

POLAR HIGH-PRESSURE CAP

60° LOW-PRESSURE BELT

30° HIGH-PRESSURE BELT (HORSE LATITUDES)

EQUATORIAL LOW-PRESSURE BELT (DOLDRUMS)

30° HIGH-PRESSURE BELT (HORSE LATITUDES)

60° LOW-PRESSURE BELT

POLAR HIGH-PRESSURE CAP

BELTS OF PRESSURE

Heat is airlifted and passed along from the tropics to the poles by this system of wind cells. In the process, some general patterns of weather evolve. Where air currents have a tendency to flow downward, as at the poles, high-pressure areas are fairly constant. Where air circulation is upward—for example, at 60° latitude—a predictable band of low pressure occurs. Again, descending air at the junction of the mid-latitude and tropic belts creates the zone of high pressure and light winds which for centuries has been colloquially known as the horse latitudes. Rising tropic air near the equator accounts for the low-pressure area called the doldrums. Here, because the movement of the air is generally vertical, the equatorial seas are calm—disturbed only occasionally by fitful winds that do not blow for long in any one direction.

The Curving Coriolis Effect

STRAIGHT LINES BENT BY SPIN
The Coriolis effect can be demonstrated using a phonograph turntable (of the free-turning variety), a cardboard disc with a map of the Northern Hemisphere, and a pencil and ruler.

In the 19th Century, G. G. Coriolis, a French mathematician, observed that an object moving across a turning surface veers to the right or left, depending on the direction of rotation. Thus, as the earth spins toward the east all moving objects in the Northern Hemisphere tend to veer to the right, and in the Southern Hemisphere to the left. A jet plane flying to New York from Seattle would, if this so-called Coriolis effect were not compensated for, land in South America as the earth spins under it. The winds are also deflected by this rotation. Instead of blowing due north or south, they become prevailing easterlies and westerlies. *(right)*.

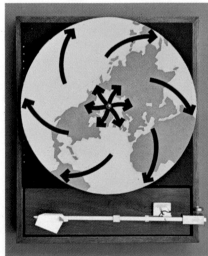

(1) With the North Pole placed over the spindle, the turntable is spun counterclockwise, which is the direction of the earth's spin in the Northern Hemisphere. A line drawn along the straight edge of a stationary ruler describes an arc, owing to the fact that the turntable is moving.

(2) When a series of lines is drawn from the pole (the spindle) to the equator (at the rim), they all curve to the right, or west. Thus the earth's rotation deflects the southerly trending winds of the tropic and polar air cells and bends them into a sweeping flow toward the west.

(3) The westward sweep of winds in the tropic and polar air cells is reversed in the middle-latitude cell (which is shown blank on the map). In this region the air movement is generally northward, with the result that the Coriolis effect bends these winds into an eastward flow.

EQUATOR

70

PREVAILING WESTERLIES

HORSE LATITUDES

TRADE WINDS

A Land-Sea Cycle of Winds

Winds are driven not only by the temperature difference between the warm tropic and the frigid polar regions, but also by contrasts between land and sea air. Land masses lose or gain heat rapidly, seas gradually. The difference can be felt on any hot day in a coastal area. The land heats quickly, expanding the air and creating a low-pressure area which is filled by cooler air blowing in from the sea. When the sun sets the land cools, and the wind reverses direction.

This cycle is dramatically intensified when the temperature of an entire continent comes into seasonal contrast with that of the sea. The Asian monsoon is basically a land-sea wind that operates on a seasonal basis, because the land retains and loses its heat on a six-month, rather than a 24-hour, cycle. During the summer the monsoon blows from sea to land *(opposite)*, in winter from land to sea. The direction of these seasonal winds is so predictable that First Century sailors, lacking a compass, relied on the Asian monsoon to guide them on their trade route from Egypt to the distant coast of India.

AN ONSHORE BREEZE
The sails of outrigger canoes billow before the landward breeze that blows toward the Philippine coast during the day. Comparable winds often relieve sweltering coastal cities in the U.S. on hot summer days, causing the temperature to drop as much as 10°. A similar process, on a continental scale, produces the seasonal monsoon winds shown in the diagram at right.

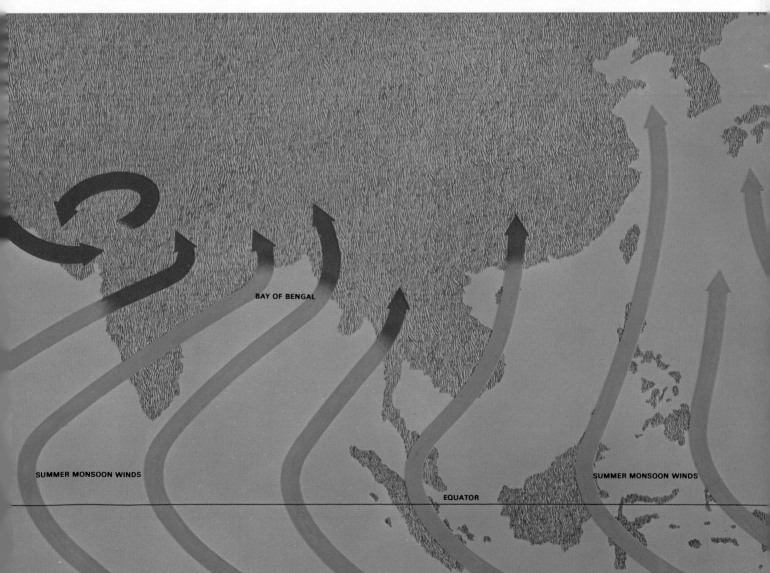

LAND-HEATED AIR

MOIST SEA AIR

THE SUMMER MONSOON PATTERN

The drawing above shows the general pattern of a summer monsoon. Cool sea air *(blue)*, heated by the land, is lifted and moved forward until turned back by a mountain range. In eastern Asia *(below)*, the monsoon sweeps in during late spring, bringing eagerly awaited rains —as much as 280 inches to the coastal mountains of India. The heaviest rainfall descends over the funnel-shaped area at the head of the Bay of Bengal. Here wet winds, suddenly forced upward by the rise of the Khasi Hills, bring an annual deluge of more than 400 inches.

BAY OF BENGAL

SUMMER MONSOON WINDS

SUMMER MONSOON WINDS

EQUATOR

Conflicting Armies of Air

Unlike other areas—such as the subcontinent of Southeast Asia—where the air masses that dominate wind and weather are seasonal, North America is a region of constant conflict. Here, four different types of air masses from six regions are forever vying to dominate the weather. This clashing of air masses helps account for the changeability of U.S. weather.

Not only does each of these air masses bring a change in temperature and humidity, but each generally has its own pattern of wind as well. The crisp dry weather characteristic of continental polar air usually is ush-ered in by northwest winds which sweep away haze and pollutants *(bottom, opposite)*. Maritime tropical air brings warm, muggy conditions, usually on southerly winds. In this air, smoke does not rise, so pollutants hug the ground *(top, opposite)*. The weather associated with maritime polar air, which usually packs northerly winds, brings low clouds, fog and drizzle—the weather common in the Pacific Northwest in summer. Relatively light winds characterize the hot, dry continental tropical air mass, which dominates the Southwest during the warm months.

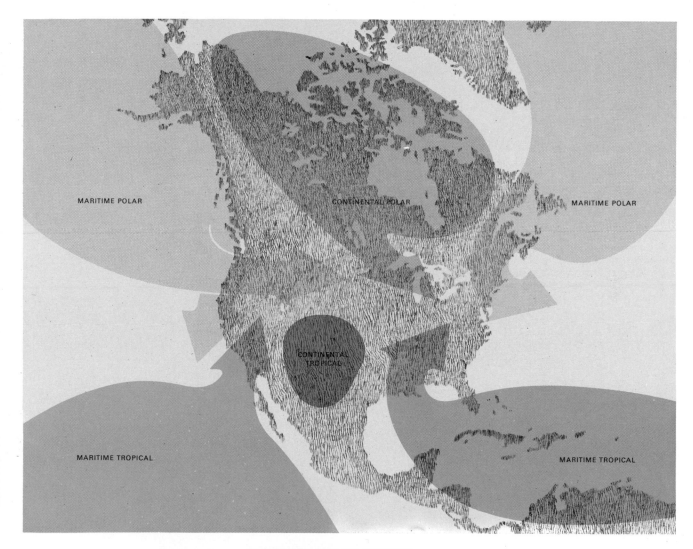

MARITIME POLAR

CONTINENTAL POLAR

MARITIME POLAR

CONTINENTAL TROPICAL

MARITIME TROPICAL

MARITIME TROPICAL

HIDDEN AND REVEALED
In two views, the skyscrapers of Manhattan, seen from the top of the R.C.A. Building, are shrouded with haze *(top, opposite)* as moist, maritime tropical air moves in from the sea, and *(below)* emerge with crystal clarity as crisp, dry continental polar air sweeps across the city.

AIR MASSES FOR ALL SEASONS
At various times, these six air masses influence Northern Hemisphere weather. Some are largely seasonal; during spring, for example, the sun melts northern snowfields, and the breeding ground of the continental polar air mass shrinks to half its winter size. Another change occurs in the south during the winter, when the continental tropical air mass vanishes completely.

Powerful Streams of Air Aloft

When the B-29 Superfortress came into service toward the end of World War II, flying at higher altitudes than any bomber had ever flown before, its pilots made a startling discovery. On certain routes, their aircraft, which had an average ground speed of 350 mph, were slowed by as much as 200 mph. Meteorologists, investigating, found that the planes were encountering previously unknown high-altitude winds, traveling at better than hurricane speed. They named these winds "jet streams."

Since then, experts have charted these winds. They have found that jet streams girdle the earth in wavelike patterns from west to east, and that they generally occur high above the border where cool and warm air masses meet. When the temperature contrast between air masses is sharp, as in winter, jet streams may move at more than 300 miles per hour; when the contrast is slight, as in summer, they slow down to mere gale velocity. Jet streams often give impetus to storms near the surface of the earth.

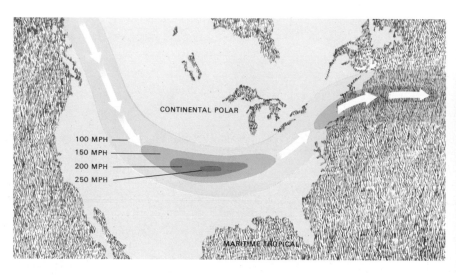

A JET STREAM'S LOOPING ROUTE

The wintertime path of a North American jet stream swoops down above the leading edge of a polar air mass, forming a ribbon of wind 300 miles wide, four miles deep. The stream tends to be fastest where the polar front penetrates deepest into the warm air to the south, because it is along this line between air masses that extreme temperature contrasts occur.

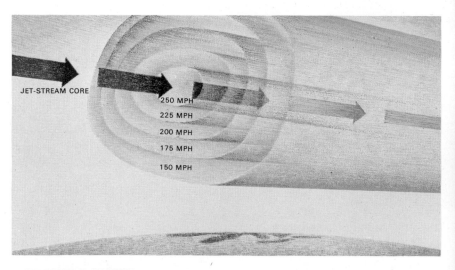

A JET-STREAM PROFILE

This diagram shows a cross section of a jet stream over the Midwest, with the Great Lakes on the horizon. Within the stream, speed is greatest at the core, with velocities falling off rapidly both vertically and horizontally. Airplanes sometimes seek out such a current to get additional speed—but flight across a jet stream may subject a plane to great strains.

FORCE TO STOP A FORTRESS
A B-29 Superfortress, the first bomber to cruise regularly at 30,000 feet, flies in jet-stream territory. During World War II, B-29s heading for Japan from Pacific island bases were frequently forced to return to their bases after encountering the fierce head winds of a jet stream.

CLOUD SIGNS OF A JET STREAM
Like all winds, jet streams are invisible, but sometimes their effects can be seen when their passage creates a disturbance in high-altitude clouds. In the picture below, cirrus streamers form wavelike curls in the turbulence set up by the 100-mph fringe winds of a jet stream.

A FEARSOME ARRAY OF TWISTERS
Six tornadoes, in various stages of formation, funnel down in this artist's reconstruction of a situation that brought devastation to three states in May 1955. A severe cold front collided with a mass of hot, sultry air over parts of Texas, Oklahoma and Kansas. Nineteen separate tornadoes were spawned in a single day, leaving 114 dead and more than 700 injured.

Tornado: Wind in a Whirlpool

The most violent winds on earth are those that spin in the funnel cloud of a tornado. Moving as fast as 500 mph, these deadly coils of wind pack a doubly destructive power: their winds at the outer edges can hurl aside almost anything in their path; within the funnel, the air pressure is so low that houses explode from the pressure of expanding air inside them.

Tornadoes, most of which occur in the U.S. Midwest, are bred by colliding air masses. According to one theory, fast-moving cold, dry air overruns moist, tropical air—instead of wedging under, as usually happens —creating a tremendous imbalance. The warm air rushes upward, sometimes at 200 mph. Air flowing in from the sides gives the updrafts a twist. The vortex begins to spin, accompanied by rain or hail and almost continuous flashes of lightning. Tornadoes travel at up to 40 mph, and usually last only a few minutes. But those minutes can be catastrophic.

AN OMINOUS COLUMN OF WIND
Whirling swiftly, the funnel of a tornado sweeps toward a small Canadian town. The roar of the storm alerted a local photographer, who snapped the funnel just before it veered away from Main Street. In its one-minute visit, it smashed barns and unroofed houses but it caused no injuries.

4
The Saturated Skies

PRECIPITATION AT PURDUE
Caught in an unusual autumn downpour, Purdue football fans huddle under their umbrellas. Heavy fall rains are rare in the Midwest because there is not usually enough cool Canadian air to precipitate moisture from saturated air moving up from the Gulf of Mexico. On this Saturday afternoon, a premature mass of cold air from the north triggered the cloudburst.

As surely as spring precedes summer, clouds precede the fall of water on the face of the earth. Although water is present in some degree almost everywhere in the atmosphere, it is usually unseen, in the form of vapor. Clouds are patches of the air's water content made visible, giving clues about the weather to come.

Man has always looked on clouds and their life-giving downpour of rain with awe, as part of the majesty of creation. Sometimes he has tried to influence them with religious ceremony and magic, but without much success. As the voice of Jehovah scornfully asked Job from the whirlwind, "Canst thou lift up thy voice to the clouds, that abundance of waters may cover thee?"

But if man still cannot control the formation of clouds and the fall of rain, except in the puniest way, he can at least watch them coming. Much of the pageantry of weather is the pageantry of clouds moving across the sky. Of the three main ingredients in a day's weather—heat, wind and water—water is the only one of the three that is actually visible even some of the time.

It was apparent to the earliest hunters, farmers and mariners that clouds were harbingers of weather. Cloud folklore is far too ancient to trace to its origins. A weather book written in the Third Century B.C. by Theophrastus, a pupil of Aristotle's, warned that certain clouds were sometimes signs of rain. The English language abounds in old adages concerning clouds and weather. For example, mountainous clouds in the morning were considered dependable signs of rain to come: "In the morning mountains / In the evening fountains."

But the men of past centuries could only conjecture at the reasons why raindrops, snowflakes, sleet or hail fall from clouds. Plutarch observed that a big battle is often followed by rain, and the theory that warfare somehow causes rain has probably revived with every war since; it was still flourishing in the muddy trenches of World War I. Explanations have ranged from the belief that offended gods like to clean up carnage promptly through the theory that rain-stimulating vapors rise from the blood and sweat of soldiers to the suggestion that the waters are shaken from the clouds by the noise of cannon. In the early 1910s the cereal magnate C. W. Post tested this last theory by bombing clouds with dynamite over a period of years in Battle Creek, Michigan. Showers sometimes fell, but it usually rained elsewhere too, without benefit of bombs. On one occasion, while congratulating himself on his success, he was informed that it had rained that day from the Pacific Coast to the Great Lakes.

It was not until the 19th Century that scientific light was first shed on clouds. The American meteorologist James P. Espy declared in 1830 that there was a connection between convection—the rising of warm air—and the condensation of atmospheric vapor. Later meteorologists began to explore the exact physical processes involved in condensation and in precipitation—the fall of water from the sky to the ground. The processes proved harder to unravel than anyone had supposed.

Today, meteorologists have more interest than ever in the problems posed by clouds. They believe that these ephemeral, airborne masses of microscopic water droplets will help them find the way to their most important goals: more accurate forecasts, and eventual control or modification of the weather. They are spending more time, effort and dollars on the study of clouds and cloud physics than on any other aspect of meteorological research.

A new look at the clouds

For centuries all men ever had was an earthbound view of clouds, but now the meteorologists' view of them is positively Jovian. Observers fly under, through and over them in airplanes, capture cloud droplets on glass slides filmed over with oil or soot—each droplet so minute that it takes a million of them to make a raindrop—and subject them to microscopic study. Balloons and light beams determine the altitude of clouds, and radar locates storm clouds too far away to see, plots their shape from top to bottom, and keeps track of their growth and movement.

In 1959 cloud-watching literally reached new heights when photographs of the earth's cloud cover were taken from a missile 700 miles out in space. For the first time, a global sweep of clouds was seen, reaching from Florida to the African coast, from the mouth of the Amazon to the North Atlantic. Since April 1960, Tiros weather satellites have relayed millions of informative pictures of cloud cover from heights of about 450 miles, making possible the global cloud maps that are now routine in weather analysis and forecasting.

Clouds are water in transition—a crucial stage in the earth's majestic hydrologic cycle, in which an estimated 95,000 cubic miles of water circulate between earth and sky each year. Of this total, some 80,000 cubic miles are evaporated off the oceans and 15,000 cubic miles from land—from lakes, rivers, moist earth and vegetation. The atmosphere carries this moisture about and eventually returns it to earth again as rain, snow, sleet or hail, or as frost or dew. The average annual rainfall around the world is an estimated 40 inches. About a quarter of it—an estimated 24,000 cubic miles—falls on land. Thus, luckily for humans, the waters of the earth are distributed and the land receives from the air more than it originally gives.

The total rainfall on land is enough to provide every man, woman and child with an average of more than 22,000 gallons of pure rainwater every day—a superabundance even on an increasingly more crowded earth. But as always, averages are deceptive. Where the rain falls depends on

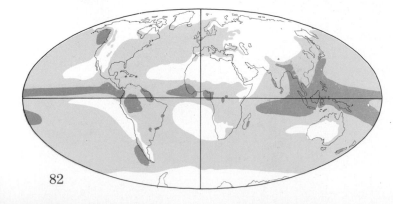

UNDER 20 INCHES

20 TO 80 INCHES

OVER 80 INCHES

WORLD RAINFALL and its distribution, indicated by different-colored areas in the map at left, depend on patterns of wind and pressure. The low-pressure belt at the equator is an area of abundant moisture and heavy rain. Where mountains push the winds upward, yearly rainfall also tends to be heavy. But continental interiors, cut off from the sea by mountains or distance, are usually dry.

82

geographical factors and global winds. The amount of rainfall varies from less than an inch a year in some desert areas to the torrential 470 inches that pour down each year, on the average, on Mount Waialeale in Hawaii, the rainiest spot on earth. In America, the spread ranges from a meager 1.7 inches in California's Death Valley to a copious 140 to 150 inches in coastal areas of the Pacific Northwest, only 800 miles away.

Most condensation—whether it is the appearance of a miniature breath-cloud on a winter's day or the formation of a towering summer thunder-head—results from the cooling of water vapor. Under normal atmospheric conditions, there is a simple relationship between temperature and the capacity of water to remain in a highly energetic, vaporous state. The higher the temperature of the vapor, the faster its molecules move. When the molecules are moving fast enough, many of them can cram into a given space without sticking to nearby solid objects or to one another; thus warm air can contain a great many vapor molecules. But if the air is cooled, the molecules slow down, and as they strike surfaces, bits of dust or other molecules, they tend to stick. The vapor begins to condense.

The amount of vapor present determines the temperature at which condensation occurs. If relatively few molecules of vapor are present, they are less apt to collide even at low temperatures. If the air is crowded with vapor molecules, they will condense at higher temperatures. The temperature at which a given amount of vapor in a body of air will condense is called its dew point.

One other factor besides temperature and quantity of water influences atmospheric condensation. This is the presence of a surface or particle on which water can condense. In the absence of such objects, condensation is drastically slowed. In laboratory experiments, researchers have crammed astonishing amounts of vapor into a vacuum, or into carefully filtered air, before condensation began—more than four times the amount that would begin to condense in the same volume of particle-filled air.

Landing fields for molecules

The surfaces that abound at earth level often act as cooling agents for the surrounding air. Large drops readily form on them without going through any intermediary cloud stage. Water molecules which touch the surfaces tend to stick—and once stuck they attract more molecules. In a familiar household example of this process, the vapor from a hot shower strikes a cool surface—such as the bathroom mirror—and coats it with beads of moisture. At night, in the same fashion, large drops of dew quickly gather on every cooling blade and leaf. In very cold weather, vapor may condense directly into ice crystals; frost coats the ground and covers windowpanes with delicate patterns.

High above the ground, there are no such cooling surfaces. Nevertheless, the atmosphere swarms with tiny particles of foreign matter, around which water may condense. These "condensation nuclei" are present everywhere in varying amounts, from 100 per cubic inch far over the oceans to 65 million per cubic inch in polluted city air. Salt particles provide effective and numerous condensation nuclei. They are produced by the evaporation of sea spray and are distributed all over the world by global winds. The many fires that occur on earth also fill the air with chemical particles. They rise in the smoke from forest fires, factory chimneys, automobile exhausts and the like, and also serve as condensation nuclei. Dust, most of it from soil and rocks, constitutes a third large category. The effectiveness of these particles as condensation nuclei depends on their size and the capacity of water molecules to adhere to them, but as far as is known, every patch of air in the troposphere contains enough nuclei so that vapor will condense at or near the normal dew point.

Earthbound clouds

Humans can see this process at work in the formation of a fog—which is simply a cloud that occurs near the earth. Ground fogs often form in damp pockets at night—in river valleys, over streams and bottomlands —after the earth has radiated away much of the daytime heat. Fog may also form when warm, damp air blows over the cool earth at night, or over the surface of the cool sea. In either case, damp air is chilled to its dew point. Molecules of water fasten on airborne nuclei floating nearby. The droplets so formed are quite different from dewdrops, as anyone can tell from the feel of them on the face, or the look of them as they float about. Billions upon billions of them swirl through the air, but they do not readily coalesce unless they strike a surface and stick. Thus in the midst of the fog, large drops march along a windowsill or spangle coat collars and hair.

The most familiar clouds, of course, appear high above the earth. They are formed when moist air is pushed upward and is cooled by the process of expansion. Its vapor content reaches the dew point and begins to condense on surrounding nuclei. The tiny droplets, some as small as .0004 inch in diameter, fall very slowly, the air's resistance just balancing their minuscule weight.

Clouds present ever-changing skyscapes of infinite variety and significance. To understand them and the weather they portend, it helps to know their names. The international classification system used by the World Meteorological Organization (WMO) is based on one devised in the early 19th Century by an English chemist and Quaker, Luke Howard. Howard divided clouds into three fundamental classes, according to their appearance to ground observers: *cirrus* (Latin for "curl of hair"), *stratus* ("spread out") and *cumulus* ("pile").

A DISCOMFORT FORMULA for hot, humid weather is given in the chart below. Called the temperature-humidity index *(curved line),* the formula is based on the relationship between air temperature *(bottom line)* and relative humidity, which reflects the air's degree of saturation *(top line)*. To determine the index, a line *(penciled at center)* is drawn between the temperature and humidity readings; the point at which it crosses the curved line determines the temperature-humidity index. The higher the index reading, the more uncomfortable the average person will be.

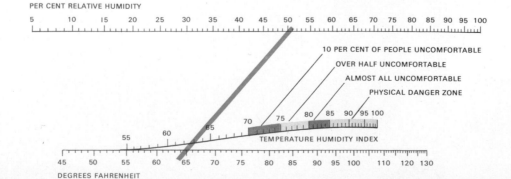

PER CENT RELATIVE HUMIDITY

5   10   15   20   25   30   35   40   45   50   55   60   65   70   75   80   85   90   95   100

10 PER CENT OF PEOPLE UNCOMFORTABLE

OVER HALF UNCOMFORTABLE

ALMOST ALL UNCOMFORTABLE

PHYSICAL DANGER ZONE

70   75   80   85   90   95   100

55   60   65

TEMPERATURE HUMIDITY INDEX

45   50   55   60   65   70   75   80   85   90   95   100   110   120   130

DEGREES FAHRENHEIT

Cirrus refers to high clouds, appearing from about 20,000 feet on up. These atmospheric regions are so cold that cirrus clouds are composed of ice crystals rather than water droplets. Unlike clouds composed of liquid droplets, they are hazy in outline and delicate in appearance, resembling wisps of hair or light, feather strokes of zinc white from an artist's brush.

Stratus clouds come in layers or broad sheets, more or less uniform in contour and color.

Cumulus clouds, sometimes called cauliflower clouds, are conspicuous for their vertical development. Their tops are usually dome-shaped, perhaps with billowy knobs, while their bases are flat, and they often travel sedately in flocks across the sky. Single cumulus clouds pile majestically upward in towering castles and sky-mountains.

Although these are the main categories, clouds can rarely be pigeonholed into them neatly. Cloud-cataloguers have had to invent combined names to describe the many variations of cloud that actually occur. For example, rolling masses of gray and white clouds that cover large areas of the sky, particularly in winter, are called stratocumulus clouds. A high, spreading cover of cirrus may be called cirrostratus. The Latin word *nimbus* ("rain cloud") is often added to indicate the cloud is precipitating: thus stratus clouds from which rain or snow is falling are called nimbostratus; dark, towering cumulus clouds, sometimes called thunderheads because they breed storms, are cumulonimbus.

The rising of moisture-laden air that results in the formation of clouds is caused by three things, operating singly or in combination: hills or mountains, a wedge of underlying cold air and, finally, heat, which generates an upward convection current.

The cloud-capped mountains

When air is lifted by sloping terrain, the increasing altitude causes it to expand and cool. The vapor it carries reaches its dew point, condenses on nuclei and turns into clouds. This process occasionally leads to unusual phenomena. A single mountain, like New Hampshire's Mount Washington, may be so high that it wears a cloud, called a cloudcap, on its summit more or less permanently. Sometimes a range will regularly wring all the moisture out of the skies on its windward side, leaving the land to leeward parched; thus deserts lie at the foot of many of the eastern slopes of the Sierra Nevada. When hot, dry winds, such as the Rocky Mountain chinook, the Alpine *föhn* or the Andean *zonda*, sweep down from the mountains across the land, it is sometimes possible to stand in the leeward valley and see the moisture draining away above. Seething masses of cumulus clouds loom behind the mountaintops; they have come to be called the *föhn* wall.

A second mechanism for lifting warm air is a moving wedge of cold air.

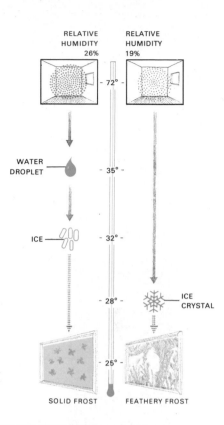

FROST PATTERNS on a windowpane are affected by the amount of moisture in the atmosphere. Two samples of air—one measuring a relative humidity of 26 per cent at 72° F. *(left)*, the other a relative humidity of only 19 per cent *(right)* are cooled. The moister air reaches its dew point at 35° F., at which point water vapor begins to condense into droplets. Further cooling starts these droplets freezing at 32° F. But for the drier air the temperature must drop below freezing before condensation begins. Then water vapor turns directly into crystals of ice. On windowpanes *(bottom)* this difference causes varying patterns of frost—a flat sheet of ice at left, and a feathery pattern of crystals at right.

In the United States, dense polar air masses, arched like vast inverted bowls over perhaps a million square miles of territory, regularly move south from the North Pacific, Canada and the North Atlantic. Just as regularly, moist, light, tropical air masses travel north from the Pacific, the Gulf of Mexico and the Caribbean. U.S. weather maps are a daily chronicle of the meeting and mixing, waxing and waning of these masses.

When two contrasting air masses meet face on, the sloping boundary between them is called a front. When a tropical air mass displaces a polar air mass, the boundary is called a warm front; when cold air displaces a warm air mass, it is called a cold front. Each kind of front generates a characteristic sequence of weather. It is not necessary to have a weather map with fronts drawn on it to tell what is happening. It is possible to look up and read the drama of the clouds.

The coming of a front

A city may be sitting comfortably in the middle of an inverted bowl of polar air which has brought a spell of fine summer weather—of clear blue skies and cool, dry air—when a mass of moisture-laden tropical air begins pushing north. The warm air rides up over the denser polar air somewhat like wind driving up a mountain slope. As it rises, it cools. As it cools, its water vapor condenses into clouds.

The warm front first reveals its presence to watchers at its leading edge, at the very top of the inverted bowl, with high, feathery wisps of cirrus clouds, perhaps 40,000 feet high. The clouds mark the boundary between the warm and cold masses. From overhead, the front slants downward to the rim of the bowl of cold air beyond the horizon, perhaps some 400 to 500 miles away.

As the cold air retreats, the warm front moves steadily forward at the rate of 10 to 15 miles per hour. As it does so, it brings progressively lower clouds. The lofty cirrus gives way first to high cirrostratus, then to altostratus or altocumulus—stratus or cumulus clouds at middle altitudes. Rain may fall at this point, and the atmosphere becomes noticeably warmer and more humid. Finally warm air approaches at ground level, accompanied by low-hanging nimbostratus clouds—heavy, turbid layers bringing steady rain. The next day the sun breaks through the layers and a warm spell begins.

When a cold front advances, quite a different sequence of clouds and weather crosses overhead. The mass of cold, dense air bears down on the mass of warm, humid air, plowing under it and lifting it up, much as a snow shovel pushes under its burden of snow. There is often no warning of its coming; the cold is suddenly present at ground level. A cold front may cause more violent weather than a warm front, but it has its compensations—the bad weather lasts a shorter time. As the front moves

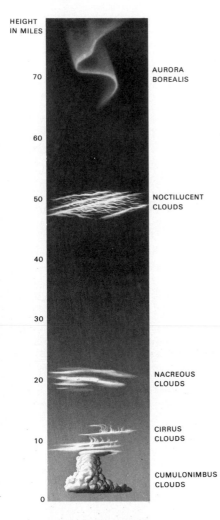

HEIGHT
IN MILES

70 — AURORA BOREALIS

60

50 — NOCTILUCENT CLOUDS

40

30

20 — NACREOUS CLOUDS

10 — CIRRUS CLOUDS

— CUMULONIMBUS CLOUDS

0

THE HIGHEST CLOUDS, seen only in the same polar or subpolar regions where auroras occur most frequently, are the noctilucent (literally "night-shining") clouds. Forming at a height of about 50 miles, noctilucent clouds get their name from the fact that they are visible only during the twilight hours. Some meteorologists think these clouds consist of crystals of ice formed on tiny particles of dust from space. Below the noctilucent clouds are shown nacreous ("mother-of-pearl") clouds—rare clouds of unknown origin —cirrus clouds, the highest of the ordinary clouds, and cumulonimbus, or thunderheads.

in, the warm air is thrown turbulently upward, often forming towering cumulonimbus clouds that produce violent thunderstorms or extremely heavy showers. Then the sun shines once more, and for a few days the storm clouds are succeeded by so-called fair-weather cumulus clouds that sail white and puffy overhead against a dazzling sky.

Fair-weather cumulus is usually generated by convection caused by ground-level heating. Tall, turreted cumulus clouds, often tens of thousands of feet high, rise over warm bodies of land or water; smaller, less dramatic ones appear over man-made "hot spots"—plowed fields, sprawling industrial complexes, the sun-baked pavements and masonry of metropolitan areas.

Good weather usually generates only pure, fluffy cumulus clouds, but on a hot, muggy day, a huge, lowering cumulonimbus cloud may form even without the presence of a cold front, piling up so high that ice crystals form at the top, spread out into a distinctive anvil shape by high-altitude winds. Such a cloud can be enormous: six miles or more in diameter and six miles high, containing upward of half a million tons of water. The ominous appearance of cumulonimbus clouds is only a pale reflection of the violent events going on inside them. Miles high, warm at the bottom and cold at the top, they generate both tremendous updrafts and violent downdrafts, sometimes moving at speeds of 200 feet per second, as warm air shoots up and rain shoots down.

The downpour characteristic of the cumulonimbus raises a pertinent question. What causes precipitation? Cloud droplets are so tiny and the resistance of air so great that the droplets easily ride in the sky. If they collide, they tend to bounce off one another unless they are extra-large. What process brings a million of them together into one raindrop or snowflake heavy enough to fall to earth? Meteorologists puzzle more over how water ever gets down from the skies than over how it gets up.

Nobody is certain of the answer, and there is even some disagreement over the theories. Among one group of meteorologists, for example, there is a growing conviction that atmospheric electricity is somehow involved in the creation of precipitation. But most meteorologists believe rainfall occurs in one of two ways, depending on the temperatures of the cloud and the nature of the nuclei it contains.

Rain that falls in splashes

First, warm rain that falls in huge, splashy drops is believed to be caused by a coalescence of the tiny droplets. This is believed to account for tropical rains that cascade from cumulus clouds whose summits are at temperatures considerably above freezing. In hot latitudes, convective currents are particularly strong. Cloud droplets churn upward at a great rate, and they also drift lightly downward at the upper limits of the

WIND SWEEPING UPWARD over high terrain often forms clouds, as airborne water vapor is cooled and condensed by its rapid ascent. The drawings below show three examples of these orographic, or mountain-bred, clouds. At left, in the Cascades, rising humid air has formed piled-up bands of cirrocumulus. At center, rapid condensation over a South Atlantic island causes turbulence which is visible in hook-shaped wave clouds. Over the Antarctic island at right, a laminated cloud is formed from an upthrust wind stream made of alternate layers of moist and dry air.

MOUNT RAINIER

GOUGH ISLAND

HEARD ISLAND

updraft. The chances of collision are great. Salt crystals, common in tropic air, offer large nuclei, so that some of the cloud's droplets tend to be slightly larger—and therefore faster-falling—than the average. The falling droplets collide with smaller ones in their downward path and coalesce. The enlarged drops begin to fall at an ever-faster rate, sweeping up more droplets on their way. Eventually they grow large enough and heavy enough to fall out of the cloud as raindrops.

From ice crystal to raindrop

The second way raindrops form accounts for most rainfall in the temperate zones. It was first suggested in the mid-1930s by a Swedish meteorologist, Tor Bergeron. Bergeron wished to explain the fall of rain from clouds in which trillions upon trillions of tiny droplets float gently, without the larger droplets that characterize the formation of heavy tropical rains. He reasoned that something in the midst of this swarm must pull the droplets together in order for rain to begin. He considered every process he could think of—including electrical attraction—and eliminated all but one as being too inefficient or too slow. He knew that ice crystals, for complex thermodynamic reasons, cause surrounding water droplets to evaporate; the vapor then freezes on the crystals. Ice crystals in the midst of a cloud would qualify as the catalyst necessary to produce rain. In 1935, Bergeron published a paper proposing the astonishing theory that most rain begins as snow.

His theory was later elaborated by a German physicist, Walter Findeisen, and is now widely accepted as the Bergeron-Findeisen theory of rain. It rests on the fact that most rain clouds have some ice crystals in their upper altitudes even in temperate weather. Only a few crystals need be present to start the process. Curiously, minute amounts of pure water, such as exist in clouds, do not ordinarily freeze at 32°F., even when they are condensed on foreign nuclei. They remain a "supercooled" liquid. It has been found in laboratories that such droplets can remain liquid until they cool to −40°F., at which point they all freeze in a rush. However, among all the nuclei in a cloud, a few are impurities that promote freezing at higher temperatures. In almost any cloud whose temperatures at the top are below 32°F., a few ice crystals will form. Around every crystal, droplets evaporate and the ice crystal is enlarged. Crystals may be outnumbered by droplets a million to one, but they cut such a swathe through the surrounding moisture that in the end they triumph. It has been estimated that a snowflake large enough to fall at an appreciable rate can form from a million supercooled cloud droplets in about 10 minutes.

Meteorologists are now persuaded that almost all precipitation except tropical rain begins as these rapidly fattening ice crystals. As the

FOR PROTECTION FROM RAIN, the umbrella became fashionable in the 18th Century, although it had been used in Europe as a sunshade since the 16th Century. The French dandy pictured in this early-19th Century engraving is sporting a folding bumbershoot, equipped with a collapsible case which he carries in his pocket.

crystals grow, they fall and collect more drops, and occasionally another fattened ice crystal. If the weather is cold all the way to the ground, they may arrive as aggregations of crystals, in the incredibly dainty form of snowflakes. Or they may leave the cloud as flakes, hit a layer of warm air several thousand feet above the earth, melt, then strike cold air again near the ground, refreeze and land as the ice pellets we call sleet. But most often the crystals melt, stay melted, and come to earth as rain.

Hail, the final form of precipitation, is the peculiar product of thunderclouds. According to the most widely held theory, hailstones form when ice crystals are caught in the great updrafts and downdrafts that sweep from the raining bottoms to the freezing tops of thunderclouds six to 10 miles high. Alternately melting at the bottom of each ride and refreezing at the top, the hailstones collect more water on each trip until they become heavy enough to fall to earth. If a hailstone is carefully sliced in half, it will be apparent that it is formed, like an onion, of concentric layers. Each layer is the record of an eventful journey to the freezing summit of the cloud.

A ghastly demonstration of this process was provided in 1930 by five German glider pilots who soared into a thunderhead in the Rhön Mountains. Swept into the cloud's vertical air-shuttle, and afraid their fragile aircraft would be torn apart, all five bailed out and opened their parachutes. The updrafts immediately bore them to regions of freezing temperatures and pelting hail. They become human hailstones, falling, rising and freezing. When they finally fell to earth, four of them were frozen stiff. Only the fifth survived.

Among real hailstones, accounts of giants are legion. The official U.S. record is held by one that fell in Potter, Nebraska, in 1928. It measured 17 inches in circumference and weighed one and a half pounds. During the storm that produced this monster, hailstones fell with such impact that many of them were buried in the ground. In other storms, hailstones have killed humans and caused untold damage.

The first cloud-seeding

The ice-crystal theory of rain has led to man's most hopeful attempts to influence the behavior of clouds since primitive man danced his first rain dance. The artificial seeding of rain clouds was developed in 1946 by General Electric's Vincent J. Schaefer and Irving Langmuir. The principle behind it seems a model of logic and simplicity: to introduce into a cloud of supercooled droplets an agent that promotes the formation of ice crystals. Two agents are commonly used. One is silver iodide, whose crystalline structure is similar to that of natural ice and therefore provides hospitable nuclei on which ice crystals readily form. The

TRYING TO MAKE RAIN with explosives carried aloft by a balloon, the man in this engraving sets off a blast with an electric apparatus and is rewarded by a shower. The picture appeared in an 1880 *Scientific American* article titled "Novel Method of Precipitating Rain Falls." Invented by Daniel Ruggles, the device was granted a patent.

other agent is solid carbon dioxide, or dry ice, which is so cold that it causes water vapor to solidify into enormous numbers of tiny ice crystals. In either case, precipitation should follow, according to the Bergeron-Findeisen theory. Pellets of dry ice are usually sown into a cloud from airplanes. Silver iodide is released as smoke, sometimes from an airplane, sometimes from the ground.

Artificial seeding was launched in a wave of optimism. Many farmers and ranchers tried it during the '40s, often with more enthusiasm than good sense. One meteorologist tells of a young pilot who flew aloft and dropped a lump of dry ice overboard—right through the greenhouse roof of the farmer who had hired him.

By now, however, years of experience have led to a more hardheaded evaluation of rainmaking's effectiveness. The truth is that when rainfall in seeded areas is carefully compared with rainfall in "control" areas, it is almost impossible to tell whether the cloud produced rain because it was seeded or because it was about to rain anyway. The most that can be said is that certain clouds already loaded with moisture do seem amenable to seeding. But scientists are a long way from producing abundant rain where and when it is needed. For some time to come, precipitation seems likely to fall when and where nature wills it, and man will just have to make the best of it, as he always has.

The Mechanics of Rainfall

Rain is the great atmospheric equalizer. Its cycle of evaporation-condensation-precipitation provides a global transfer of two vital quantities—moisture and heat—from places of oversupply to places where they are needed. Water is lifted from the seas and distributed to fields and rivers. Heat is taken into the atmosphere by evaporation, mainly from the tropics; the tropics are thus made livable and their heat, redistributed, makes the rest of the world livable as well. This process produces staggering statistics. One third of all solar energy reaching the earth is expended in evaporating water; the amount of water involved is about 95,000 cubic miles a year—105 quadrillion gallons. Between the time a drop of water evaporates into the atmosphere and the time it precipitates back to earth, it may travel thousands of miles. And no less than one billion tons of water rains down on the earth every minute of the day, in a deluge of Biblical proportions.

THE HIGH COST OF WET GROUNDS
In a pouring rain, groundkeepers pull a huge tarpaulin over the baseball diamond at Chicago's Comiskey Park. Rain is a costly weather phenomenon for baseball; in a recent season it caused postponements 71 times. In the 1962 World Series four games were rained out—at a cost of $500,000, borne by the two clubs, television, the airlines and various other affected enterprises.

The Kinds of Precipitation

All precipitation begins with the cooling and condensing of water vapor. The form in which precipitation finally reaches the earth depends on three variables: air currents, temperature and humidity. This diagram shows the processes involved. Ordinarily, precipitation begins with water vapor condensing on tiny nuclei, often particles of salt. Cloud droplets are thus formed. In Column 1, the cloud droplets coalesce into raindrops. In 2, the process starts the same way, but freezing air intervenes and solidifies the raindrops into sleet. In 3, the drops, falling on frozen ground, become glaze, or freezing rain. In Column 4, frigid air crystallizes a droplet (or often water vapor itself). The resulting crystal grows as it falls, finally reaching earth as a snowflake. In 5, a similar snowflake meets warm air as it falls earthward, softens, clumps to other wet flakes and ends up a big wet snowflake, perhaps an inch across. In 6, the warm air is a little warmer—and it melts the snowflake into rain. In 7, the cloud droplet freezes. But as it falls, an updraft throws it back aloft, where more droplets freeze onto the kernel. It falls again, collects more water and freezes, growing all the time. Finally it hits the ground as a hailstone.

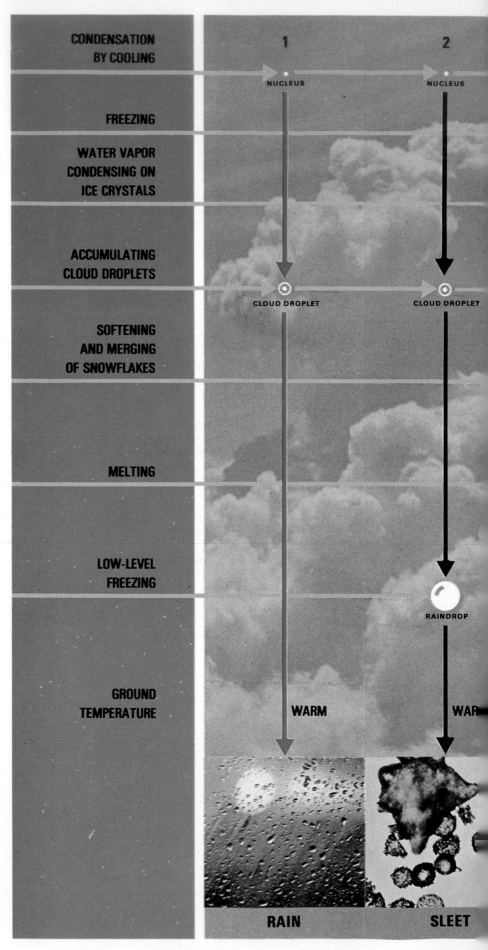

CONDENSATION BY COOLING

FREEZING

WATER VAPOR CONDENSING ON ICE CRYSTALS

ACCUMULATING CLOUD DROPLETS

SOFTENING AND MERGING OF SNOWFLAKES

MELTING

LOW-LEVEL FREEZING

GROUND TEMPERATURE

1   2

NUCLEUS   NUCLEUS

CLOUD DROPLET   CLOUD DROPLET

RAINDROP

WARM   WAR

RAIN   SLEET

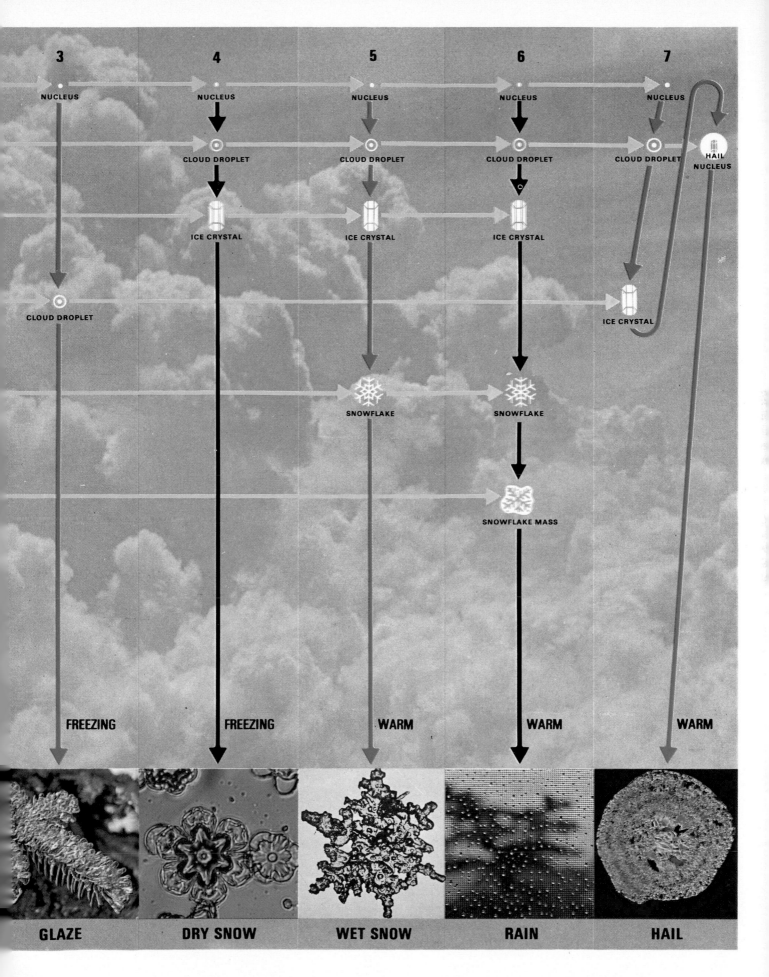

3

NUCLEUS

CLOUD DROPLET

FREEZING

GLAZE

4

NUCLEUS

CLOUD DROPLET

ICE CRYSTAL

FREEZING

DRY SNOW

5

NUCLEUS

CLOUD DROPLET

ICE CRYSTAL

SNOWFLAKE

WARM

WET SNOW

6

NUCLEUS

CLOUD DROPLET

ICE CRYSTAL

SNOWFLAKE

SNOWFLAKE MASS

WARM

RAIN

7

NUCLEUS

CLOUD DROPLET

HAIL NUCLEUS

ICE CRYSTAL

WARM

HAIL

War of the Air: The Cold Front

Toward the end of World War I, deprived of the usual foreign weather reports, which were withheld for military reasons, neutral Norwegian meteorologists sought new techniques of forecasting. They refined the concept that weather was created largely by movements of masses of air. Borrowing from battleground terminology, they named the point where two air masses met and clashed the "front." The page opposite shows a cold front—that is, the leading edge of a cold air mass which is driving into a mass of warm air. The result of this meeting is a brief but violent thunderstorm, as the warm air is uplifted and replaced by the cold.

GENESIS OF A THUNDERHEAD

The storm shown above, a "convective storm," is similar to the frontal thunderstorm (opposite) except for the manner in which it came into existence. The sun, beating down on an open field, created a patch of warm air above it. The heated air floated upward. Then it expanded and cooled, and a cumulus cloud developed (left). More heated air kept rushing upward, enlarging the cloud (right). As the cloud approached 25,000 feet, the water droplets in it reached such a size that the updraft of air could no longer support them and they fell as rain.

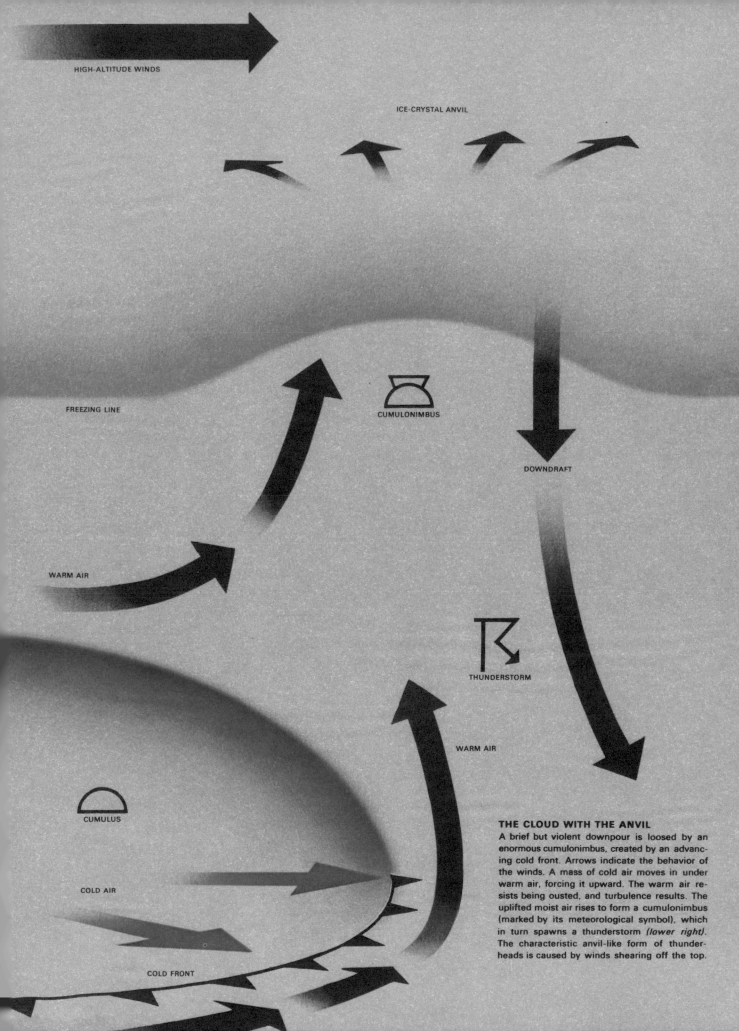

HIGH-ALTITUDE WINDS

ICE-CRYSTAL ANVIL

FREEZING LINE

CUMULONIMBUS

DOWNDRAFT

WARM AIR

THUNDERSTORM

WARM AIR

CUMULUS

COLD AIR

COLD FRONT

THE CLOUD WITH THE ANVIL
A brief but violent downpour is loosed by an
enormous cumulonimbus, created by an advancing cold front. Arrows indicate the behavior of
the winds. A mass of cold air moves in under
warm air, forcing it upward. The warm air resists being ousted, and turbulence results. The
uplifted moist air rises to form a cumulonimbus
(marked by its meteorological symbol), which
in turn spawns a thunderstorm *(lower right)*.
The characteristic anvil-like form of thunderheads is caused by winds shearing off the top.

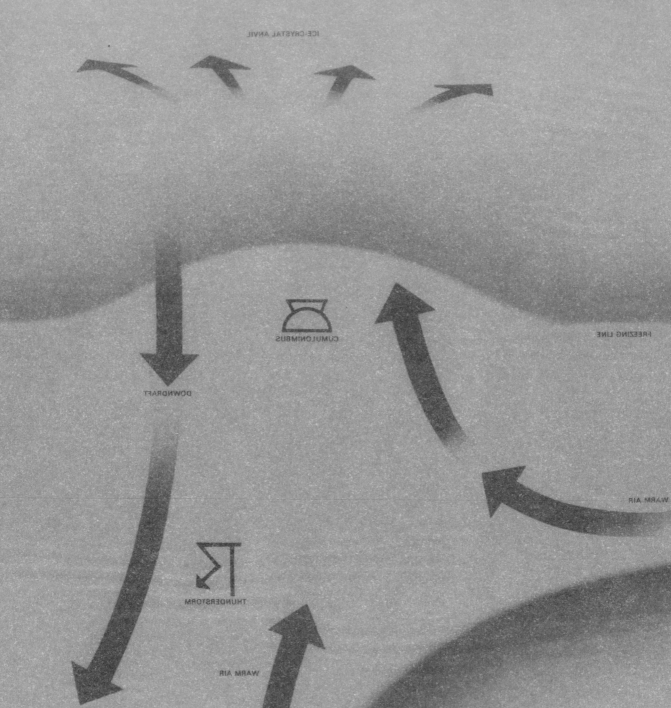
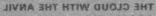

A brief but violent downpour is loosed by an enormous cumulonimbus, created by an advancing cold front. Arrows indicate the behavior of the winds. A mass of cold air moves in under warm air, forcing it upward. The warm air resists being ousted, and turbulence results. The uplifted moist air rises to form a cumulonimbus (marked by its meteorological symbol), which in turn spawns a thunderstorm (lower right). The characteristic anvil-like form of thunderheads is caused by winds shearing off the top.

War of the Air: The Warm Front

The advance of a typical warm front is more gradual and less dramatic than that of a cold front. But they both bring bad weather. The most notable characteristic of a newly arriving warm front is a flat layer of dull, gray clouds in the van, frequently accompanied by a monotonously steady light rain. Warm fronts arriving in winter often account for damaging storms. Rain falling on freezing ground turns to ice that snaps tree limbs, downs electric power lines and makes glazed highways hazardous.

THE SUN WEARS A HALO
A halo around the sun indicates an advancing warm front. It is caused by scattering of sun rays through ice crystals in the accompanying clouds. Of this, Zuñi Indians say, "When the sun is in his house, it will rain soon." They are generally right. Warm fronts usually bring rain.

THE PARADOXICAL CIRRUS
The cobwebby wispiness of cirrus clouds betrays the invasion of a warm front. Paradoxically, though cirrus clouds are frequently the precursors of warm weather, they are themselves the coldest of clouds. Because they often rise to heights of 40,000 feet, the moisture contained in them is frozen into ice crystals. High-altitude winds account for the spindrift effect.

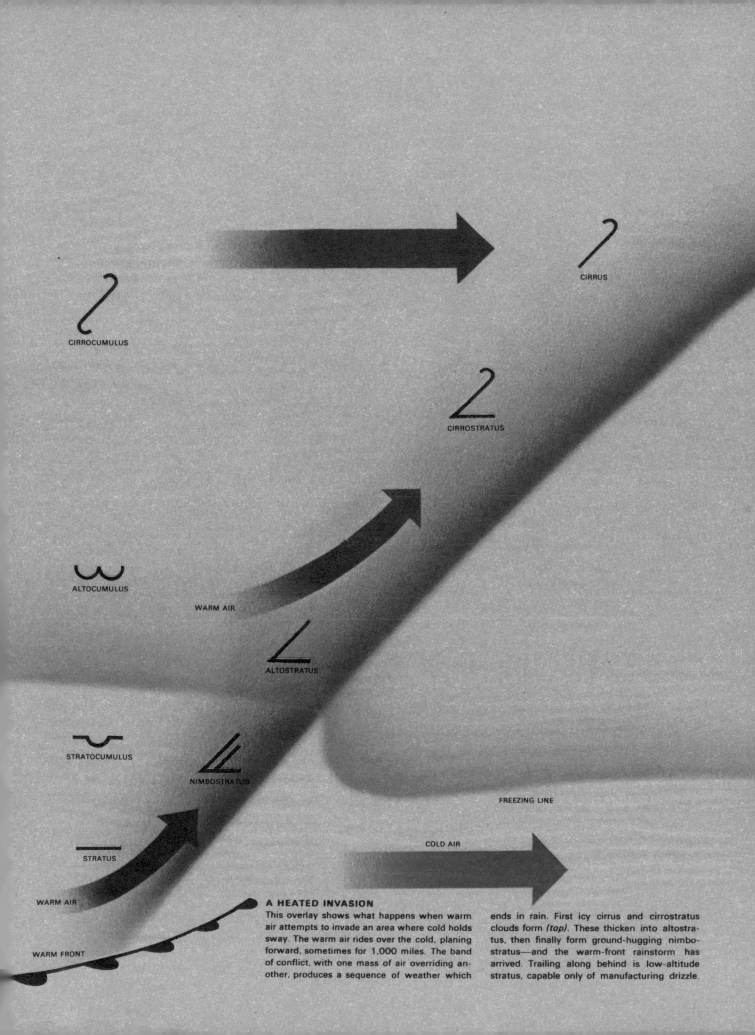

CIRRUS

CIRROCUMULUS

CIRROSTRATUS

WARM AIR

ALTOCUMULUS

ALTOSTRATUS

STRATOCUMULUS

NIMBOSTRATUS

FREEZING LINE

COLD AIR

STRATUS

WARM AIR

A HEATED INVASION

This overlay shows what happens when warm air attempts to invade an area where cold holds sway. The warm air rides over the cold, planing forward, sometimes for 1,000 miles. The band of conflict, with one mass of air overriding another, produces a sequence of weather which ends in rain. First icy cirrus and cirrostratus clouds form *(top)*. These thicken into altostratus, then finally form ground-hugging nimbostratus—and the warm-front rainstorm has arrived. Trailing along behind is low-altitude stratus, capable only of manufacturing drizzle.

WARM FRONT

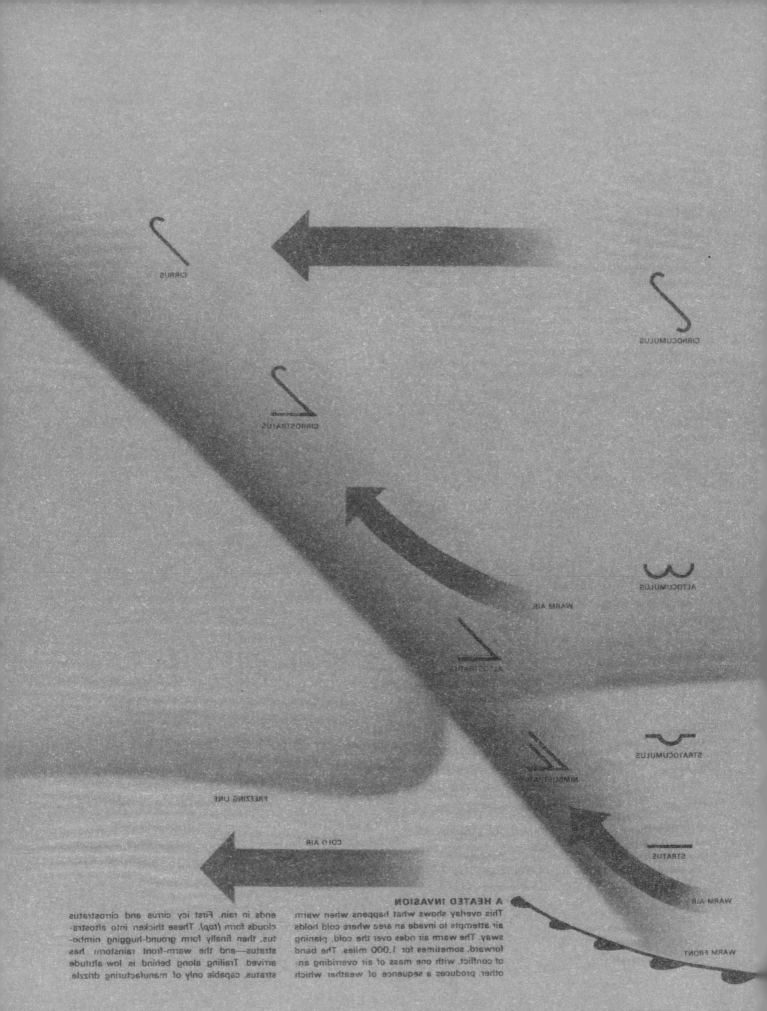

MOIST AIR

PRECIPITATION

DRY AIR

Air That Climbs the Mountains

Mountains are an important local factor in the making of weather. Moisture-laden air currents, generated by global forces, are forced upward by mountains in their path, and the moisture condenses and falls as rain or snow. Depicted here is this so-called orographic effect (from the Greek *oros*, "mountain") as seen in the U.S. West. Prevailing westerlies, hitting the mountains, are driven upward. With this rise in altitude they cool and precipitate the moisture they evaporated from the Pacific. Once they have cleared the mountaintops, these winds, now composed of air that is parched and thin, slide downward. Not only do they fail to bring any rain to the leeward slopes; they evaporate what little moisture the ground may hold. Indians in the West call such winds snow eaters. Blowing across a snowfield, they can evaporate snow at the rate of two feet a day.

MOUNTAINS AND METEOROLOGY
This drawing shows schematically the interaction of wind and topography working together to influence weather. The rainy windward slope of this mountain is lush with greenery; the sun-parched leeward slope is desert. In the U.S., such contrasts are found in the Pacific Northwest.

MAROONED ON A MOUNTAIN
The sleek streamliner *City of San Francisco* sits motionless and marooned in huge drifts of orographically produced snow near Donner Pass, California, in the Sierra Nevada, January 1952. The blizzard was the result of cold, wet air from the Pacific being uplifted by the mountains.

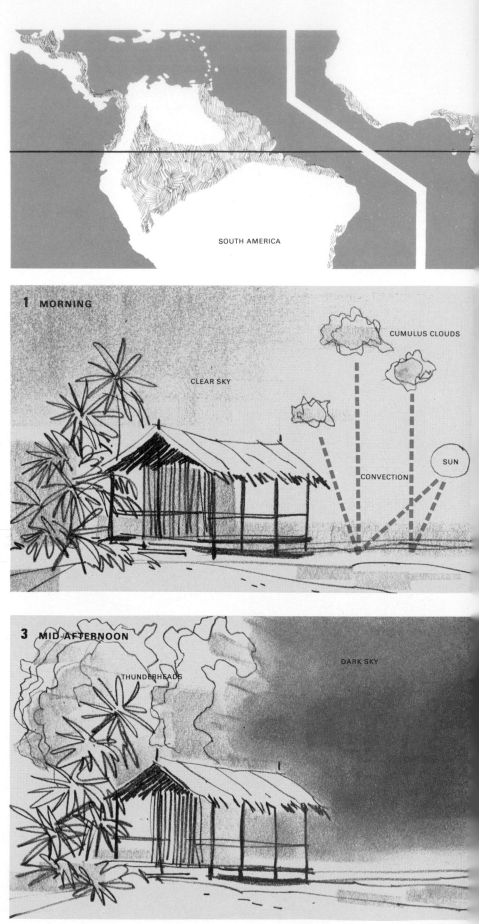

SOUTH AMERICA

1 MORNING

CUMULUS CLOUDS

CLEAR SKY

CONVECTION

SUN

3 MID-AFTERNOON

THUNDERHEADS

DARK SKY

The Land of Continual Rain

In most of the world, rain falls seasonally. But in the wet equatorial region, exemplified by the basin of the Amazon, rain falls on a fixed daily schedule. Some months are wetter than others and there may be days when it does not rain at all. But there is never less than 60 inches of precipitation a year—and there may be close to 180. Temperature is also consistently high in this region, averaging 64°F. High temperature and humidity produce the luxuriant tropical rain forest, where trees grow as much as 15 feet a year and bamboo nine inches in a single day. However, the rain leaches out the earth, carrying off vital mineral compounds and leaving a brick-red soil that is practically worthless for growing food crops. Population in the region is sparse: this is one place where rainfall discourages man instead of aiding him.

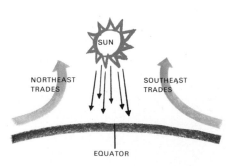

SUN

NORTHEAST TRADES

SOUTHEAST TRADES

EQUATOR

THE REASON FOR TROPICAL RAIN
This diagram explains the mechanics of the weather in the tropics. The sun, blazing down most fiercely on the region of the equator, heats the air and evaporates vast quantities of moisture. The moist, heated air rises and is cooled, its water condenses and rain descends.

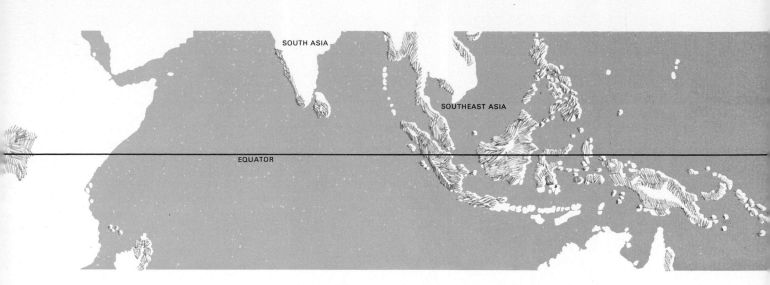

SOUTH ASIA

SOUTHEAST ASIA

EQUATOR

2 | NOON

THUNDERHEADS

EQUATORIAL WEATHER FACTORY
Contained in a belt around the equator are the areas of daily rainfall comprising the wet equatorial region *(shaded in black)*. The belt shifts somewhat in different seasons, and local topography also affects the weather—which accounts for gaps shown in the areas of heavy rainfall.

4 | LATE AFTERNOON

TROPICAL DOWNPOUR

A DAY AT THE EQUATOR
In the wet equatorial regions the daily downpour is so predictable that it occurs virtually on a regular schedule. By 9 a.m. *(Figure 1)* heat from the sun has evaporated water left on the ground by the previous day's rain, forming new moisture-packed cumulus clouds. By noon the temperature has risen 12° to 18°, humidity is becoming noticeable and the innocent cumulus is starting to shape up into an ominous thunderhead. By 3 p.m. the heat is stifling, and the sun has evaporated more water into the air, which is now approaching the saturation point. Clouds have begun to thicken, and now cover a good portion of the sky. At 5 p.m. the heavens open up to release a downpour lasting an hour or two. The rain stops as quickly as it began. The sky clears, the temperature and humidity are lower. The cycle is ready to begin again the next day.

101

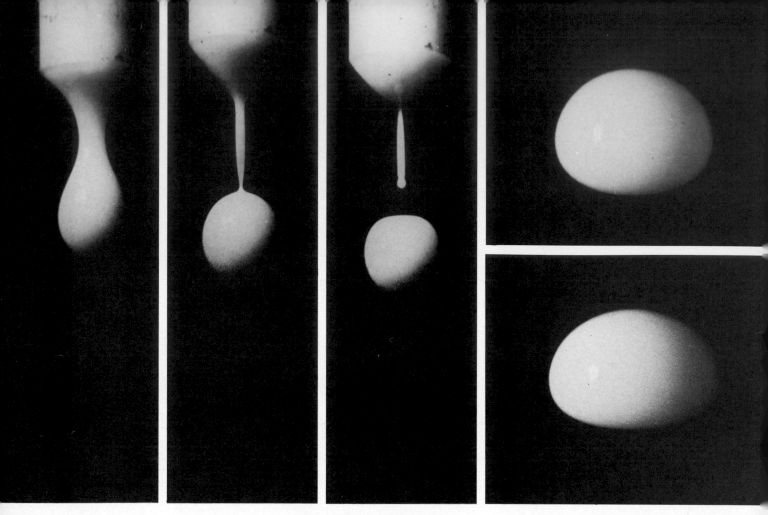

DESCENT OF A RAINDROP

Stop-action photographs record the shape of a falling drop (milk is used in this experiment because it photographs well, but rain acts the same way). As the drop starts to fall from the end of a pipette it is spherical; but as it descends, it meets air resistance that distorts it into a hamburger-bun shape. Never does it assume the teardrop shape specified in folklore.

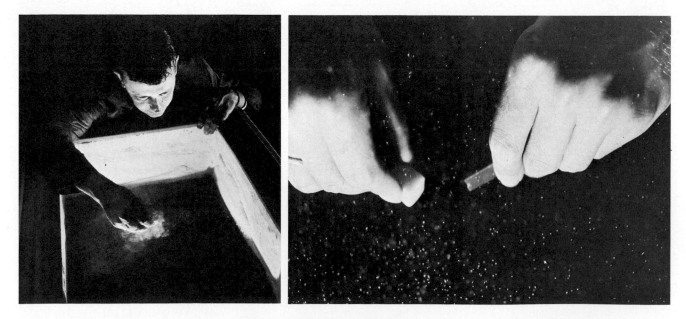

CLOUD-SEEDING IN A FREEZER

An early achievement in laboratory "weather-making" is shown by one of its originators, Dr. Bernard Vonnegut. Having first breathed into a freezer to produce a "cloud" of supercooled wa-ter droplets, he then chills the cloud further with shavings from a piece of dry ice. The close-up (right) illustrates how this additional cooling of the cloud produces a shower of tiny ice crystals.

Weather in the Laboratory

Utilizing crude theories about meteorology, Americans early began trying to tinker with the weather. In 1838 Pennsylvanian James P. Espy proposed to break a long drought by setting large wood fires along a north-south line on the Western frontier. The heated air, he reasoned, would rise, form clouds and precipitate a rain that would sweep eastward. In 1891, Chicago's Louis Gathman suggested rainmaking by refrigeration. His method: "Suddenly chill the atmosphere by rapid evaporation . . . of various highly compressed gases," thus condensing atmospheric moisture to produce rain.

In this century meteorologists began moving the quest for weather's secrets into the laboratory, investigating such factors as the shape of the raindrop *(opposite)* and the influence of electricity in creating rain *(below)*. In July 1946, Dr. Vincent Schaefer made a major breakthrough with the discovery of how to make clouds manufacture snow under laboratory conditions *(opposite, below)*.

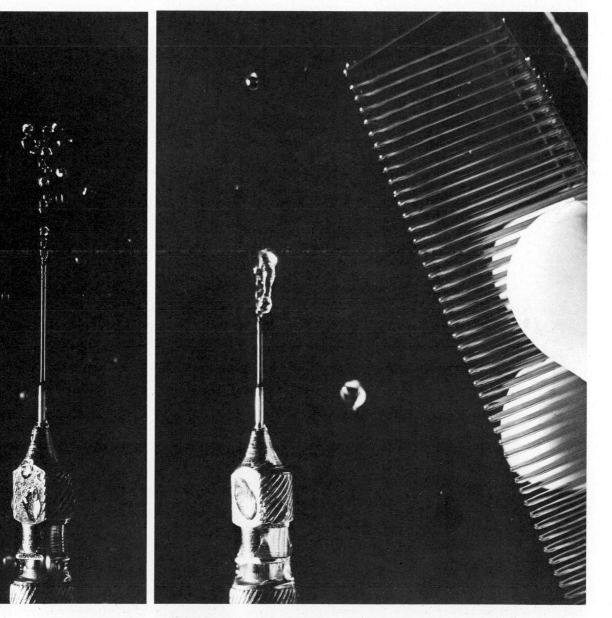

THE MAKING OF A RAINDROP
An experiment in the laboratory demonstrates the theory that in the presence of an electrical field water droplets will combine to form raindrops. Tiny droplets like those in clouds *(left)* will simply ricochet off one another under normal conditions. But in the presence of a comb charged with static electricity *(above)*, they combine and become a single large drop.

103

Wired
for Thunderbolts

Meteorologists disagree over why one rainstorm is just a rainstorm and another is a thunderstorm. But most of them believe the difference is a matter of height. In an ordinary rainstorm, moisture-laden air is lifted only to a level sufficient to squeeze out water, which falls as rain. But in a thunderstorm the moist air is carried to a much greater height, as shown below. This warm, wet air rises and condenses into a cloud. The heat released by condensation makes the air still more buoyant, so that it is forced to even higher altitudes. Then, in a game of atmospheric leapfrog, succeeding parcels of air rise higher and higher, until finally the column of air, now a thunderhead, is so high that its moisture freezes. And it is ice, it is generally conceded, which functions as the switch that turns on that powerful atmospheric generator known as a thunderstorm.

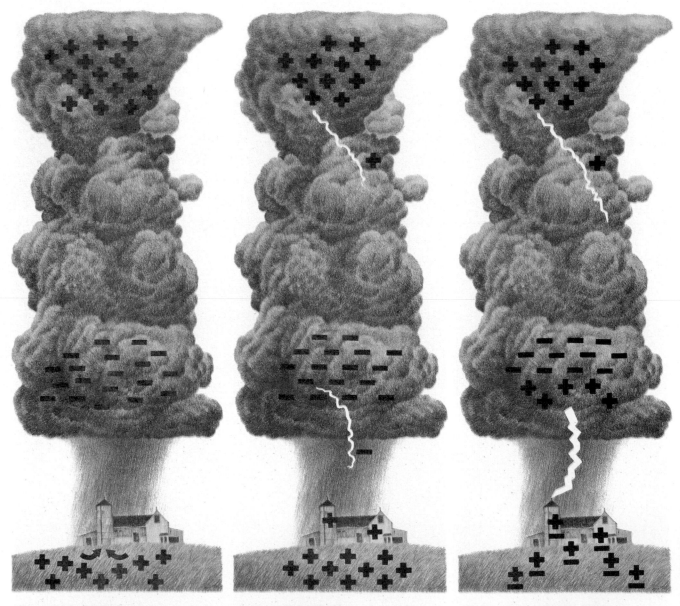

STAGE ONE: IMBALANCE

Thunderstorms, which originate because of thermal imbalances, involve complex electrical imbalances as well. Positive charges collect at the top of a forming thunderhead—and the negative charges gather below. These set up an attraction with positive charges on the ground.

STAGE TWO: BUILDUP

At first no cloud-to-ground electrical discharge can occur because the air acts as an insulator. The problem is solved when a "streamer" (indicated here as a white slash, but nearly invisible) opens up an ionized channel through the air—in effect, a wire that the electricity may follow.

STAGE THREE: DISCHARGE

The bolt strikes, and current flows from cloud to ground. Because any tall projection causes a local concentration of electric charge, the streamer is usually attracted to the highest object in the neighborhood—like a silo *(above)* or New York's Empire State Building *(opposite)*.

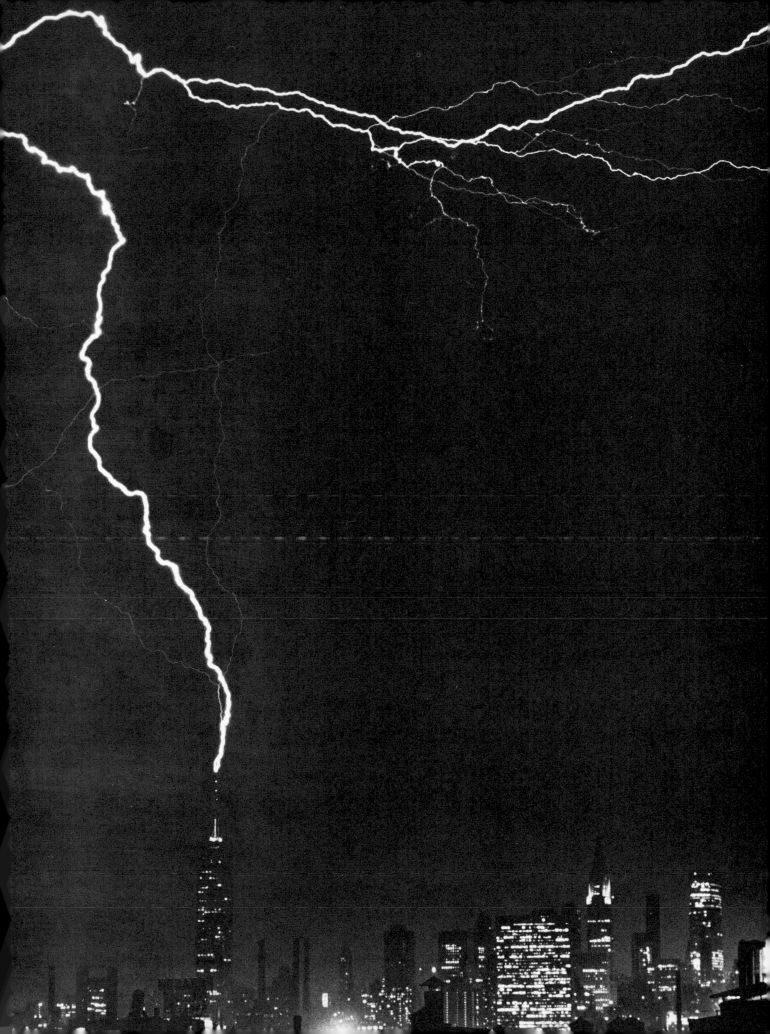

5
At the Weather's Mercy

"A THUNDERSTORM IN HAY-TIME may overthrow a ministry, and a slight rise or fall of temperature may topple a throne. . . ." With these words, in his best-selling novel *Storm*, George Stewart sums up the unpredictable effects of weather upon man and his affairs. In spite of the wonders of modern technology, man is as vulnerable to weather today as he was centuries ago—perhaps even more so. The mechanized world of the 20th Century creates more opportunities for him to be affected by it. Weather is still the great dice-shaker. Its economic effects are well known: it influences the stock market and the harvesting of corn, house-painting and the loading of ships, the sale of bathing suits and the success of a parade. It may determine the outcome of horse races, battles and love affairs. It may even affect man himself biologically, a fascinating possibility that folklore has suggested for centuries but that science has only begun to explore.

In 1579 fog hid the entrance to San Francisco Bay from the English navigator Sir Francis Drake, and may have altered the course of history. Drake and his hawk-eyed crew of the *Golden Hind* were exploring the coast for England's Elizabeth I, but missed the bay. Fog—"wandring upon the face of the earth and waters, as it were a second sea," as Sir Francis put it—lost them a landfall. It was two centuries later before another voyaging ship discovered the Golden Gate, and that luckier ship was Spanish.

Today radar would reveal the passage in an instant, through the thickest of coastal mists. But does this mean that fog is no longer a problem? Far from it. In 1952 a heavy December fog closed in on metropolitan London for four days. Before it cleared it left an estimated 4,000 people dead or dying. Sulfur dioxide and other toxic substances from industrial processes laced the fog with poison, and the fog lasted long enough to have disastrous effects on thousands of respiratory systems.

In late 1667 a pamphlet entitled *Strange News from Virginia* was published in London, describing "the Dreadful Hurry Cane" that had battered the 60-year-old English colony of Jamestown during August and September of that year. The storm began, the account says, on August 27, "and continued with such Violence, that it overturned many Houses, burying in the Ruins much Goods and many people, beating to the ground such as were any wayes employed in the Fields, blowing many Cattle that were near the Sea or Rivers, into them, whereby unknown numbers have perished, to the great affliction of all people. . . . The Sea (by the violence of the winds) swelled twelve foot above its usual height, drowning the whole Country before it, with many of the Inhabitants, their Cattle and Goods, the rest being forced to save themselves in the Mountains nearest adjoining. . . ."

Along about the same time of year in 1960, Hurricane Donna smashed its way up the Atlantic Coast from Key West to the Gulf of St. Lawrence. Advance warnings kept the death toll down to about 30, but in spite of storm-tracking radar and airborne "hurricane hunters," exposed coastal communities fared little better than colonial Jamestown. Property damage, estimated at an unprecedented one billion dollars, made Donna one of the most destructive storms in history.

In October 1846, unseasonably early snows struck the Sierra Nevada in Northern California, and caught an emigrant wagon train of trail-weary men, women and children unaware. The Donner party, California-bound, was behind schedule. They had crossed the Rockies and the salt flats of Utah and Nevada, and now, at the base of the towering Sierras, their desert-bleached, canvas-top wagons creaked to a halt. Five feet of snow choked the pass through the mountains, and even as they made camp more began to fall. It fell for eight days, burying their makeshift shelters and piling up 30- and 40-foot drifts. Hopelessly trapped and low on food, the members of the party began to die of hunger and exhaustion. In desperation they began to eat their own dead. It was not until the following February, five months later, that help reached them. By then, only 47 of the original 87 members survived.

Snowbound in Donner Pass

In the middle of January 1952, 106 years later, Donner Pass weather again played havoc with a party of travelers. In the worst storm to hit the California coast since 1890, more than seven inches of rain fell on Los Angeles in three days, and blizzards howled into the Sierras, choking mountain roads with 50-foot drifts. Heading west through the pass with 226 passengers and crewmen aboard, the steam-heated luxury train *City of San Francisco* stalled in a snowdrift. In a short time its fuel supply gave out, leaving the train without light or heat—and with only one day's supply of food. As the hours ticked by and the temperature dropped, crewmen rationed out the contents of the pantry and passengers broke up Pullman ladders for bonfires in the steel-floored vestibules. Meanwhile an army of snow-fighters struggled toward the helpless streamliner. But it was three days before the victims were rescued.

Weather has always played a key role in warfare, and sometimes a decisive one. Hannibal took the Alpine snows into account when he planned the march on Rome, and Napoleon failed to allow for the Russian snows when he marched on Moscow. Sometimes weather so clearly tips the scales of battle that it is no wonder soldiers see a divine will at work in it, for or against them. The famous 19th Century Prussian general, Karl von Clausewitz, whose classic book *On War* sought to reduce warfare to a science, nevertheless conceded that weather injects an element of chance into the best-laid military plans. Fog, he wrote, "prevents the

CALIFORNIAN
"THE WORLD IS GOVERNED TOO MUCH."
MONTEREY, SATURDAY, MARCH, 27, 1847.

Cache Creek, Feb. 5th, 18—

By the arrival of the Brig Francisca, 3 days from Yerba Buena, Le Moine, Master, brings to us the heart rending news of the extreme suffering of a party of emigrants who were left on the other side of the California mountain, about 60 in all, nineteen of whom started to come into the valley. Seven, only have arrived, the remainder died, and the survivers were kept alive by eating the dead bodies. Among the survivers are two young girls.

A public meeting was held at Yerba Buena, and about eight hundred dollars raised for the relief of the sufferers who still remain in the mountains, Messers Ward and Smith kindly offered the use of their Launch, and a party under direction of Pas'd Midshipman Woodworth with the intention of disembarking at the foot of the mountain and then going on foot, with packs of provisions. It is to be hoped they will succeed in reaching them with sufficient provisions to get them in.

We have but few of the particulars of the hardships which they have suffered. Such a state of things will probably never again occur, from the fact, that the road is now better known, and the emigrants will hereafter start and travel so as to cross the mountain by the 1st of October, The party which are suffering so much, lost their work cattle on the salt plains, on *Hasting's cut off*, a rout which we hope no one will ever attempt again.

A WINTER WEATHER TRAGEDY is told in this contemporary account of the fate that befell the Donner party. It appeared in the Monterey *Californian* on March 27, 1847.

enemy from being discovered in time, a gun from firing at the right moment, a report from reaching the general," while rain "prevents one battalion from arriving at all, and another from arriving at the right time, because it had to march perhaps eight hours instead of three. . . ."

In January 1777, during the early, critical days of the American Revolution, a fortunate cold snap came to the aid of George Washington in his campaign against the British garrisoned at Princeton. Washington was trapped at Trenton, amid an unseasonable thaw that had turned the roads to deep mud and prevented him from moving his army. And then suddenly on January 2 the wind shifted to the northwest and the roads began to freeze. By 1 a.m. they were frozen hard. Washington immediately seized the opportunity to take the offensive. He slipped out of the trap, marched his army 12 miles to the outskirts of Princeton in the dead of night, and caught the British by surprise. The victory not only heartened the colonists; it also increased Washington's stature at home and abroad, and may have had a decisive effect on the entire American cause.

Providential weather also played a most important role in Operation Overlord, the Allied invasion of Normandy in 1944 during the second World War. The Allied high command had given its weather experts a list of ideal weather and tide conditions for each of the military operations involved in the invasion plan. When, it asked, were these requirements most likely to be met—in May, June or July? And when would the tides be right? After analyzing the weather history of the Normandy coast, the meteorologists picked June, and notified the high command that the tides would be at their best on the 5th and 18th. The high command settled on the 5th, but then delayed until the 6th because of storms. Even then the weather was hardly what they'd hoped for: the sky was drizzly and overcast, and the sea choppy. Nevertheless in retrospect the choice was a blessing. The Germans, doubting that the Allies would launch an invasion in such marginal weather, were caught completely off guard. And on June 20th the worst storm in 20 years lashed the Normandy beaches. Weeks later the Allied weathermen sent Eisenhower a memo about it. "Thanks," Eisenhower dashed across the memo, "and thank the gods of war that we went when we did."

A cause of sniffles and suicides

The most profound of weather's effects upon man is the role that it plays in his personal life, through its influence on his body, mind and emotions. In many cases the connection is obvious and clearly biological: when a cold "norther" hits the normally tropical Central American highlands, many Indians contract fatal pneumonia; in the temperate zone of North America, the changeable weather of early spring invariably ushers in the head cold. But some experts believe weather may also

AMONG THE GREAT EVENTS which weather has affected, perhaps none was more decisive than the 13th Century invasion of Japan by Kublai Khan's forces. The Japanese fought valiantly to keep the Mongols from landing (right), and held them to beachheads. Then a typhoon—ever since called the Kamikaze, or Divine Wind—roared in, sinking more of the Mongol fleet and ending the invasion attempt. During World War II, Japanese suicide pilots were called Kamikazes.

109

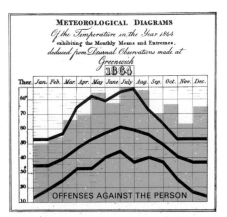

TEMPERATURE AND CRIME are correlated in this graph drawn from statistics compiled in London for the year 1864. The three lines represent the low, average and high temperatures for each month. The bars stand for the number of people arrested for criminal offenses. The fewest arrests (624) were made in January, the most (1,243) in July.

influence man in far more complex, obscure and fascinating ways.

Since the late 19th Century—when the formal study of the effects of environment on personality first became organized—science has probed the connection between weather and a variety of human activities, from the frequency of cases of assault and battery to the classroom deportment of children, from the circulation of nonfiction in public libraries to suicides, and from the commission of mayhem and murder to the making of love. Data on all of these subjects are contained in a voluminously detailed book, *Mainsprings of Civilization*, written by the late Dr. Ellsworth Huntington of Yale. In humid weather in Denver, Colorado, schoolchildren had to be disciplined five times more often than they did in dry weather. In public libraries in eight cities in North America, people withdrew books of serious nonfiction much more frequently in late winter and early spring than at other times of the year.

In his book *Climate Makes the Man*, Dr. Clarence A. Mills, Professor of Experimental Medicine at the University of Cincinnati, claims that bad moods and falling barometers go hand in hand. On a day when the humidity is low and the barometer is rising, the average man tends to go about his daily work cheerfully, function more efficiently and look upon life with optimism. But the same man on a muggy day in August growls at his children, snaps at his fellow workers, is gloomy, sullen and pessimistic. Under normal circumstances most people muddle through such weather-induced distress; perspective and a sense of humor come to their rescue. But for people whose physical condition is already below par the oppressive effects of bad weather can tip the balance from marginal health to serious illness. And for people already under emotional stress, it may trigger explosive acts of aggression.

Hot tempers in the Punjab

Of the 148 religious riots that occurred in India between 1919 and 1941, says Dr. Huntington, more than one third took place in the most uncomfortable months, April and August. The figure drops slightly in May and June, when the monsoon season brings cool winds and showers to relieve the blistering heat and parched air. But it begins to rise again in July, when the wind slacks off and the air becomes soggy.

In another classic study—by a pioneer in the field of weather influence, O. E. Dexter—weather emerged as a probable factor in assault-and-battery arrests. Studying some 40,000 such arrests in New York City, Dexter found that the rate of increase exactly paralleled the rise in temperature. In January the figure for arrests was low, in July it hit its peak—only to fall off during the devitalizing mugginess of August. "Temperature, more than any other condition," Dexter concluded, "affects the emotional states which are conducive to fighting." He may have overstated the case a bit, but his figures apparently established a clear relationship between tempers and temperature.

Winds that blow steadily and monotonously for weeks on end have long been credited with a profound influence on people. The depressing and deranging effects of the Alpine *föhn*, mentioned in Chapter 3, are only one example. In southern France, the *vent du Midi*, a warm and moist wind, is commonly held responsible for headaches, rheumatic pains, epileptic fits, asthma attacks and certain kinds of infant fever. The people of Tangiers blame headaches and feelings of oppression on the levanter, an east wind from the Mediterranean. North Africans believe that the sirocco, a hot, dusty wind that blows off the Sahara, depresses people to the point of suicide. And a nameless east wind that blows over London in November and March was actually linked by an 18th Century British court physician to regicide. This wind, the French writer Voltaire quotes the doctor as saying, caused "black melancholy to spread over the nation." Dozens of dispirited Londoners hanged themselves, animals became unruly, people grew grim and desperate. "It was literally in an east wind," the doctor told Voltaire, "that Charles I was beheaded and James II deposed."

Debris in the wake of a wind

The healthiest weather for the majority of people is not necessarily good weather. Some doctors believe that any weather condition, good or bad, may have unfortunate results if it persists too long. For one thing it is depressing simply because it is so monotonous. But it is also harmful physically; the body becomes less adaptable to change and is therefore more vulnerable to changes when they do occur. Yet frequently changing weather can also be unsettling. The foremost agency of sudden reversals in the weather, the cyclonic storm, also seems to trigger profound disturbances in men's minds and bodies. The cyclonic storms that regularly sweep down over the U.S. Midwest are described by Dr. Mills as "leaving behind them a trail of human wreckage—cases of acute appendicitis, respiratory attacks of all kinds, and suicides."

Even people not suffering from such afflictions are unsettled by these storms, Dr. Mills reports. As the storm front approaches—and the barometer falls and humidity rises—people are unaccountably bothered by "a feeling of futility, an inability to reach the usual mental efficiency or to accomplish difficult tasks." Children become irritable and petulant, adults quarrelsome and fault-finding. "Such weather," Dr. Mills cautions, "provides the most perfect background for marital outbursts."

As the storm front passes, the weather and the emotions do an about face. The humidity falls, the barometric pressure rises, the air becomes cool, clear and invigorating; peoples' spirits become buoyant and difficult tasks are accomplished with ease. It would be a fine thing, Dr. Mills concludes, if musicians and other performing artists could schedule their public appearances for such weather: audiences would invariably hear them at their best.

Apparently a great many organisms respond in some fashion to changes in humidity and atmospheric pressure. Farmers claim that the behavior of their animals warns them as much as a day in advance when a storm is approaching: normally docile horses and cows turn perverse and unruly. Dogs are said to be able to "smell" a storm coming; they grow restless and edgy, and may run away. Fishermen claim that fish bite better just before a storm. And ants, responding to some mysterious detection system of their own, scurry about as the pressure drops, shoring up their tunnels against the approaching deluge.

Some people also appear to have a sixth sense about a coming storm: it seems to function with special sharpness in the aged, the allergic, the overweight, the chronically ill and the hypersensitive. They feel it in their bones, their joints, their muscles, their sinuses, the palpitations of their hearts. They even feel it in the scars of old football injuries. Imagination? Not necessarily. Scientists have detected measurable changes within the body that correspond to changes in atmospheric pressure—especially in the old, infirm and emotionally unstable whose biological processes may be unusually sensitive. Changes in pulse and respiration rates, blood pressure, blood composition and various physical processes systematically reflect the transit of the low-pressure and high-pressure air masses that regularly precede and follow a storm.

Arthritic pains on order

In a recent two-year study at the University of Pennsylvania School of Medicine, 30 arthritic patients were sealed in room-sized climate chambers for periods of two to four weeks. Temperature and rate of air movement were changed without producing any effect on the patients. But when researchers simulated approaching storm conditions—gradually dropping pressures from 31.5 to 28.5 inches and boosting humidity from 25 to 80 per cent—the results were astonishing. Eight out of 10 patients reported stiffness and swelling in their joints, and some reported the symptoms within minutes of the change.

There are equally dramatic examples of the elation that appears to follow the breaking of a storm. Dr. Huntington reports the experience of a group of freshmen at Massachusetts State College at Amherst, who were taking an intelligence test at the time of the New England hurricane of 1938. Outside the wind howled at 80 miles per hour, the sky turned dark, trees crashed to the ground, electric power lines snapped. It was, college officials thought, the worst kind of weather for an examination, and they expected it to be mirrored in the marks. And yet, when the results came in, they showed a jump in percentile averages from 75 to a staggering 95. Apparently the storm had acted as a powerful mental stimulant, and perhaps the stimulation came from atmospheric turbulence.

Is it true that changes in atmospheric pressure affect our thoughts and feelings? If so, how does it happen? Science does not know the answer to either of these questions, but some scientists think they may have a clue. They think that the key may lie in ions—tiny, electrically charged particles of matter that exist in the atmosphere.

Some ions are positively charged, and some are negatively charged. Usually they exist in the air in a ratio of 5 positive to 4 negative. And to some scientists, this is a critical balance. Negative ions are partly composed of oxygen, which can be beneficial to the human body; positive ions are partly composed of carbon dioxide, which can be harmful.

For a number of years ionization researchers have speculated on the possibility that a greater-than-normal number of positive ions in the air might exert a measurable effect on the body's functions by slowing down its responses. Significantly, among the agents that are known to produce an imbalance of positive ions are smog and certain kinds of heating and air-conditioning equipment.

In an experiment conducted at New York University's College of Engineering, volunteers were exposed to streams of negative ions, and then given a series of tests which showed that their visual responses had perked up measurably and that they could work much harder without showing fatigue. In a similar study at the University of California, Dr. Albert P. Krueger found that an excess of negative ions caused the body's respiratory system to function better.

Two other ion researchers—Dr. C. W. Hansell, a former RCA research scientist, and Dr. Igho Kornblueh, of the Graduate Hospital of the University of Pennsylvania—have suggested that various conditions in the atmosphere itself may produce an imbalance of ions. Perhaps the air just before a storm is overloaded with positive ions, and therefore with carbon dioxide. And perhaps the balance tips the other way when the storm breaks, dumping an overload of negative ions—and oxygen—into the air. The carbon dioxide could account for the depressing biological effects, and the oxygen for the feeling of elation—since oxygen, taken straight, is a heady stimulant.

Machine-made moods

Dr. Hansell first became aware of these effects accidentally. Back in 1932 he noticed that one of his fellow scientists at RCA, who was working with a device called an electrostatic generator, went through strange reversals in mood. Sometimes the scientist finished the working day in high spirits, while on other days he was short-tempered and gloomy. Neither mood could be attributed to the actual progress of the work itself. The man noticed it too, and became curious. He began to keep track of his changing moods and found that he was cheerful when the generator was set to produce negative ions and depressed when it was set to produce positive ones. Shortly afterward, reports from systematic ionization-research studies in Europe confirmed these observations.

Hansell and Kornblueh can only speculate at how the ion balance in the earth's atmosphere changes. In the case of cyclonic storms, the changing pressure may somehow result in the presence of more of one or the other. But the depressing effects of steady winds—which, according to their theory, would also be caused by an overdose of positive ions—cannot be explained in this way. Perhaps, they suggest, the winds liberate positive ions by stirring up sand and dust.

If it is true that ions in the atmosphere affect man biologically, it is equally true that it will be a long time before he can put this information to use outside the laboratory. Mankind is not about to alter the air's ion content by manufacturing weather. For a good many years to come, man will have to cope with weather much as he has always coped with it—by accommodating to it when he must, exploiting it when he can and running away from it when it becomes intolerable.

Meteorology in Miniature

It is customary to think of weather as something vast and global, as a series of great highs and lows and frontal systems marching across a weather map, dispensing rain or sunshine over large areas of the earth. But there is another kind of weather, which exists on a small and often personal scale: the cool shadow a barn casts during a steamy summer day, the welcome windbreak a row of trees provides in a stiff winter wind, or a hothouse in which plants may grow amid freezing wastelands (opposite). This is microweather, the weather that affects us most directly, and the only kind man has been able to influence. Microweather is always local, even minute, but it is significant nonetheless. It is a citrus farmer saving his crop by lighting smudge pots on a cold night. It is a boy and his boat finding shelter from a squall in a tiny cove. Likewise, it is a movie marquee that protects a new hairdo from a shower on the afternoon before a big date.

AN ANTARCTIC HOTHOUSE
At Wilkes Station inside the Antarctic Circle, where the average outside temperature in summer is only about 30° F., a Plexiglas bubble serves as a makeshift miniature greenhouse in which radish, lettuce and tomato plants flourish and even yield some fruit. This example of man-made microweather was created more for the sake of decoration and cheer than for survival.

Learning to Live with Microweather

Many varieties of microweather occur naturally: a sandstorm, an early-morning ground fog, a snowfield on a mountainside in late spring. This kind of microweather is caused by local conditions and although man has little control over it, a knowledge of the microweather characteristics of an area can make life more pleasant.

For example, a house at the top of a hill might be buffeted by winter winds—and the result could be an inflated heating bill. But if the house were built on the leeward slope, a few feet below the crest, the hill would act as a natural windbreak. Similarly, a garden planted along the southwest side of a hill might bloom weeks earlier than another cultivated on the shadier northeast slope.

FROM SUNLIGHT TO SANDSTORM
Unaware of the gritty blast about to envelop them, picnicking sunbathers on the shores of Lake Mead near Hoover Dam relax on the beach *(top)*. A moment later *(bottom)* they are engulfed in a sudden sandstorm. Such storms occur because the hot sand rapidly heats air near the ground, creating updrafts which lift the sand and carry it along at a height of about 10 feet.

A SKI WEEKEND IN SPRING

On the eastern slopes of Mount Washington, New Hampshire, enthusiasts enjoy skiing long after the winter's end. All around them the snows have melted, but the prevailing winds have caused the snow here to pile up in drifts so deep that they may not melt until early June.

A FOGGED-IN VILLAGE

An early-morning ground fog settles in the valley village of Stevenage, England. The fog occurred when the cooling of the ground during the night caused the temperature of the air near the ground to drop to its condensation point. Such fog is soon dispelled by the sun.

Changing the Local Weather

Every time a road is built or a house erected, microweather is influenced. Individually, these changes affect the local weather only slightly. But enough roads and enough houses assembled in one area finally achieve the status of a city. With hundreds of acres of pavement and masonry to absorb and hold heat, major changes in local weather conditions may occur *(opposite)*. When these changes are combined with quantities of industrial pollution, the results may even be deadly *(below)*. Some authorities believe that in the future cities may have to be planned scientifically to help control microweather.

AN ISLAND IN THE SNOW
Acting as a windshield, this grain elevator in Boise City, Oklahoma, produces a shelterbelt of bare earth. This photograph was taken after a three-day blizzard which dropped a foot of snow and piled up drifts many feet high. Although the effects in this case were unintentional, such shelterbelts are often artificially produced by the use of snow fences or hedges.

PARIS IN THE RAIN
A single rain cloud deluges Paris, illustrating a microweather phenomenon common to cities. Daylong heat on buildings and pavements produces strong convection currents, pulling moist air from the surrounding countryside into the city. It rises and cools—and the result is rain.

A SMOG-DARKENED CITY
St. Louis in 1940 lies shrouded in smog, a type of microweather familiar to most city dwellers. Smog is the result of a temperature inversion —a local atmospheric phenomenon that occurs when temperature rises, instead of falling, as altitude increases. When it is combined with lack of wind, the inversion traps fog as well as man-made pollutants to form a noxious blanket.

THE WIND SCOOPS OF HYDERABAD
For many years the homes of Hyderabad, Pakistan, have carried wind scoops on their roofs. Faced toward the prevailing wind, they catch even the slightest breeze and funnel it inside.

A COOL SPOT IN THE CITY
City children have long known the real purpose of fire hydrants—to provide a cooling spray during hot city summers. The water cools the children and sharply reduces the temperature of the hot pavement. But most important is the cooling effect on the air through evaporation; even a passing pedestrian may find the area several degrees cooler than the next block.

120

Some Ways to Beat the Heat

Control of weather on a global scale may be centuries away, but the control of microweather is centuries old. Early man made use of natural microweather to shelter himself from the sun's heat: he rested under a tree or enjoyed the coolness of a cave. From there, it was a short step to carrying his own shade, perhaps in the form of a tuft of dry grass, as the Bindibu tribesmen of Australia do today.

Not only shade but also the circulation of air provides respite from the heat. Wind is air in circulation, and men soon learned to make use of natural breezes to cool their houses *(below)*. Today, with air conditioning, men may think themselves far better off than their ancestors. But often people still rely on primitive methods of beating the heat. Instead of the tuft of grass, there is the newspaper *(top, left)*; in place of a waterfall, a city fire hydrant *(below, left)*.

A well-bundled Moscow tot naps at −22° F.

Pockets of Warmth amidst the Cold

There is microweather in a pocket —a tiny patch of body warmth that prevents a hand from getting cold. This sort of microweather dates from man's appearance on earth. Even in those earliest times, men maintained body heat through insulation. The bundled child above is keeping warm just the way a prehistoric child did in animal skins. Complicated space suits based on the same principle keep Astronauts warm in the abysmal cold of outer space.

There is a second kind of warm microweather, created by raising the temperature of the surrounding air *(right and opposite)*. Eskimos use both methods. Outside, they stay warm wearing two layers of light but windproof insulating clothing. Inside, they remove most of their clothing, and body heat—plus the heat from a few small blubber lamps—raises the temperature of the air within the igloo.

HEAT TRAPPED IN A TENT
Airmen training as an air rescue group find shelter from the cold under a tent of parachute cloth in a cold-weather test station in New Hampshire. Although parachute material is light, it is weathertight. It thus serves both to keep the wind out and to trap the heat within.

AN OASIS FROM THE COLD

A heated open-air pool provides recreation for swimmers and refuge from the cold for shivering skiers. A feature of a resort at Mount Snow, Vermont, the pool is kept at 105° F., about the temperature of a hot bath. The warm water and the surrounding 15-foot-high glass walls create a pocket of tropical microweather in the midst of the otherwise frigid New England landscape.

123

A MECHANICAL RAINMAKER

An Australian Air Force Vampire jet releases silver iodide crystals over a rain-pregnant cloud. In a successful rainmaking experiment, the silver iodide crystals act as nuclei on which ice forms. As the ice crystals grow, they become heavy and fall, gathering more water vapor as they drop through the cloud. At lower, warmer altitudes the ice melts, forming raindrops.

Mastering the Elements

Man's arsenal of weather-influencing devices is growing constantly; one of the newer weapons, used to warm the air, is shown opposite. But efforts to control the weather are limited to comparatively small areas. For the most part, droughts, floods, hurricanes, blizzards and other major weather phenomena remain beyond man's control.

Experts believe, however, that mastery over the weather might be learned from experiments in microweather. One of the most promising methods of weather control is cloud-seeding. Recent experiments indicate it may eventually be possible to render crop- and property-damaging hailstorms impotent, and short-circuit the awesome cloud systems that are the generators of great storms.

A MANUFACTURED CLOUD

Resembling a giant smoke ring in the sky, this man-made cloud was produced by seeding cool but cloudless air with silver iodide. Manufactured clouds such as this one could prevent frost over acres of farmland by trapping heat that would otherwise be radiated into space.

FIERY END TO A FROST

Like a fiery comet, this earthbound fireball spins on its predetermined path, heating the air in an orchard to prevent fruit frostbite. The device, which consists of a long pipe on a vertical axis with gas jets at each end, can raise freezing temperatures up to 80° Fahrenheit.

6
Laws of
the Atmosphere

THOUSANDS OF YEARS AGO, understanding the weather was a simple matter of understanding what days were good for hunting and what days were not. Today it is one of the most complicated problems of modern science, involving the reduction of masses of weather data to simple terms that can be dealt with mathematically—a formidable task.

In 1946 the late John Von Neumann, one of the most brilliant and versatile mathematicians of modern times, gave the task to a computer. Computers were then comparatively untried, but Von Neumann's, the MANIAC, had just completed the stupendous calculations that resulted in the hydrogen bomb. He was casting about for another assignment worthy of the machine's amazing speed and capacity, and he found such a challenge in meteorology. In fact, he found not one, but dozens. "The hydrodynamics of meteorology," Von Neumann told a group of fellow scientists some 10 years later, "presents without doubt the most complicated series of interrelated problems not only that we know of, but that we can imagine."

Consider, for a moment, the characteristics of a given parcel of air. It has measurable pressure, temperature, density. It contains water vapor, some of which may be condensed or frozen around tiny particles of matter called nuclei. It swarms with the electrically charged atoms called ions. All these characteristics vary from instant to instant. Moreover, they interact. A change in one produces a chain reaction of changes in the others. In addition, the parcel moves as a mass—up, down, horizontally, obliquely, in circular swirls. And as it moves, it collides, intermingles and interacts with other similarly complicated air parcels.

Blend into this the force exerted by the earth's rotation, the turmoil of clashing warm and cold air masses, the churning turbulence caused by the obstruction of mountains, the drives of the global wind systems, and the thermal influence of sun and oceans. The result is a self-perpetuating chaos whose reduction to any sort of simple, logical pattern has regularly defeated even the most rational and systematic scientific research. Only in recent years, with the wizardry of electronics—taking the form of such tools as radio, radar and, above all, the computer—has real help arrived. Now, for the first time, young meteorologists on the threshold of their careers can look forward to solving within their lifetimes some of the problems that were the fascination and despair of their predecessors.

Today's meteorologists consider themselves to be physical scientists, and meteorology to be the physics and chemistry of the atmosphere. The atmosphere, they say, is an enormous and elaborate system of interacting parts, each behaving according to fixed, unchanging laws—the same laws that govern the behavior of all matter. Weather is the result of these laws, and is therefore scientifically predictable.

And yet, for many centuries the prediction of weather was based not

A PERILOUS EXPERIMENT
Lightning leaps from an iron rod, killing a Russian experimenter, Georg Wilhelm Richmann, and bowling over his assistant as they investigate the nature of lightning in 1753. The writings of Benjamin Franklin inspired this experiment, but it was a simpler technique—a kite with a key at the end of the string—that led Franklin to his discovery that lightning is electricity.

on law but on previous performance. Men saw that weather followed certain more or less predictable patterns, but they were more interested in charting the patterns than establishing the basic causes. In fact they became quite ingenious at measuring and plotting the possible course of the weather, as a later look at their tools and methods will show.

It was another group of men—some of them not even interested in weather at all—who developed the principles that became the basis for the science of meteorology. Some of these early investigators were themselves scientists—chiefly astronomers and mathematicians—but their ranks also included sea captains, glassblowers, schoolteachers, priests and even a kite-flying diplomat.

The structure of weather

In seeking to probe the mysterious forces of the atmosphere, these men fashioned instruments that sensed and measured changes in temperature, pressure, humidity and the speed of the wind. They named clouds, watched storms, rode out typhoons and hurricanes, and painstakingly logged what they felt and saw. Slowly, out of their accumulated experiences and speculations, the true nature of weather emerged. It had, they saw, organization and structure. One day's weather was the result of things that had taken place in the atmosphere on the preceding day, and the forces that produced weather were inevitable and unchangeable—in other words, natural laws.

One of the earliest of the weather theorists was the Greek philosopher Aristotle, who lived from 384 to 322 B.C. "The whole terrestrial region," wrote Aristotle in his *Meteorologica*, was composed of four "bodies": fire, air, water and earth. He believed that these bodies "are transformable one into another, and that each is potentially latent in the others." For the most part, he said, the transforming agent was the sun. From the waters of the earth it drew a cool, moist substance, and from the earth itself it drew something hot and dry, "a kind of smoke"—the stuff that "we are accustomed to call fire." This dry exhalation formed "the origin and natural substance of the winds," and was also responsible for earthquakes and comets. In combination with the cool, moist substance, it formed air. And air, as it underwent temperature changes, turned into clouds, rain, snow, frost or dew.

Aristotle even had an explanation for thunder. When a cloud cools and condenses, it forcibly ejects the wind it contains; the noise is the sound the wind makes when it hits the surrounding clouds. As for lightning, Aristotle wrote, "As a rule the ejected wind burns with a fine and gentle fire, and it is then what we call lightning."

For 2,000 years Aristotle's fanciful reasoning was taken for fact. But in 1543 the Polish astronomer Copernicus suggested that the earth was

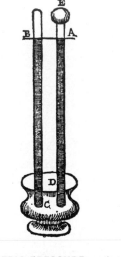

ATMOSPHERIC PRESSURE, or the weight of the air, was demonstrated experimentally in 1644 by Evangelista Torricelli. A glass tube (B) filled with mercury was inverted and its mouth inserted in a bowl of mercury. The level of mercury in the tube dropped only slightly, indicating that some force was pressing down on the mercury in the bowl: the weight of the surrounding air. The experiment was verified in a different form with another tube (A).

only a minor member of a vast solar system—and *Meteorologica*, with its earth-centered universe, gradually lost its authority. Men no longer consulted mystics and seers for information on the weather. Instead, they began to study observable facts.

Soon after Galileo had made his thermometer, around 1600, his pupil Evangelista Torricelli constructed a barometer out of a glass tube and a basin of mercury. By the end of the 15th Century there were crude but effective instruments for measuring humidity. One of the earliest, called a hygroscope, was described by the German cardinal Nicolaus de Cusa: "If you suspend from one side of a large balance a large quantity of wool, and from the other sides stones, so that they weigh equally in dry air, then you will see that when the air inclines toward dampness, the weight of the wool increases, and when it tends to dryness, it decreases."

In England, during the 17th Century, the philosopher-inventor Robert Hooke made a hygroscope that exploited the water-retaining properties of the bristle of the wild oat; he also developed an improved version of a gauge for determining the strength of the wind. Along with two other countrymen, Sir Christopher Wren and Richard Towneley, he also designed a gauge for measuring rainfall. But Hooke's most ambitious meteorological device was an elaborate assemblage of instruments which he called a weather-clock. The weather-clock measured not only time but also temperature, pressure, humidity, rainfall, and the strength and direction of the wind. Unfortunately this mechanical marvel was often in need of repairs.

Laws of the solar system

At the same time men like Galileo, the Danish astronomer Tycho Brahe, the English curate Jeremiah Horrocks and the German astronomer Johannes Kepler were conducting studies that had no immediate connection with weather, but were ultimately to play a part in the beginnings of meteorology. They were studying the behavior of the solar system—and by inference, the nature of laws that controlled it. Galileo, Brahe and Horrocks plotted distances between the earth and the sun and between the earth and the moon with greater and greater accuracy, and in 1609 Kepler showed that the earth's orbit was elliptical. Their work—particularly Kepler's—was an important influence on Sir Isaac Newton, whose *Philosophiae Naturalis Principia Mathematica*, published in 1687, is generally acclaimed to be the most stupendous achievement in the history of science.

The *Principia* argued that all matter, from the smallest particle to the largest planet, responded to certain laws of gravitation and motion. All of the *Principia's* laws are important, but the Second Law of Motion is one of the cornerstones of modern meteorology. The Second Law says

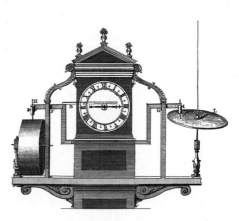

A WEATHER-CLOCK, one of the first self-registering instruments for measuring weather change, was invented in 1663 by Sir Christopher Wren, the English architect and scientist. Driven by an ordinary clock, it enabled a drumlike barometer *(left)* and a wind vane to make a penciled 12-hour record of their readings. But it took another 200 years for the science of meteorology to become sophisticated enough to utilize such devices.

that a body whose motion is changed by an outside force will accelerate in the same direction as the force, and at a rate directly proportional to the amount of the force.

But although the Second Law is important for what it says, it is almost more important for how it says it. Expressed as the mathematical equation $F = ma$ (force equals mass times acceleration) it is extremely useful to meteorologists, since force, mass and acceleration are all significant factors in the atmosphere.

But marvelous as it was, Newton's *Principia* was not enough. There were still many intricate workings of the weather that it did not explain. Key principles, key equations were missing. One of the earliest of these additional principles was discovered in the middle of the 17th Century by a contemporary of Newton's, the Irish physicist Robert Boyle. It concerns the relation between the volume of a body of air and its pressure.

According to Boyle's Law, "At constant temperature, the volume of a gas varies inversely with its pressure." In other words, if a body of air is made to decrease in size, its pressure increases, and vice versa. Inflate a toy balloon, then squeeze its air into a smaller and smaller volume; as the air is reduced in volume, its pressure rises until, squeezed enough, it will burst out of the balloon.

Then, in the late 18th Century, as an outgrowth of his studies into the nature of gases, the French physicist Jacques Charles discovered a connection between the volume of a gas and its temperature. Charles's Law says that when the pressure of a gas remains constant but its volume changes, there is an accompanying proportional change in temperature. In other words, the hotter a gas, the greater its volume. Out of the Law came mathematical equations for calculating the contraction of cooling air and the expansion of air that is being warmed. Charles's Law is sometimes attributed to another Frenchman, Joseph Gay-Lussac, who was performing similar experiments at the same time. The principle, in either case, was an extension of Boyle's Law, adding to Boyle's the important factor of temperature. Before long, it was commonly linked with Boyle's in the now classic Boyle-Charles, or General Gas, Law.

Dalton and the barometer

Shortly after the discovery of Charles's Law came the discovery of still another principle vital to meteorology. Between 1788 and 1792 an English chemist, John Dalton, conducted a number of experiments concerned with barometric pressure. Dalton was looking for connections between the behavior of the barometer and certain atmospheric conditions—rain, the direction of winds, the heating and cooling of air. Out of his investigations he formulated a law, sometimes called Dalton's Law, sometimes the Law of Partial Pressures. It says that in a mixture of gases, each gas will exert the same pressure as it would if it were alone, unmixed. It also says that the total pressure of the mixture of gases is the sum of their individual pressures. Armed with Dalton's Law, meteorologists can calculate the amount of water vapor in the air—and thus describe the formation of clouds, fog, rain and snow in mathematical terms.

From Newton to Dalton, men had discovered the laws governing most of the factors in the atmosphere that influence weather. One more principle was needed, one that stated the relationship between heat and the changes it causes in the air's temperature, pressure and volume.

Nature's indestructible energy

One of the key principles derived from Newton's system was the Law of the Conservation of Mass. It stated that mass, or matter, could be neither created nor destroyed; it could only be changed from one form to another. A blazing log does not disappear; it becomes ashes and gases. Boiling water turns into steam. In the 1840s physicists began to suspect that the same thing might be true of energy. Perhaps it, too, was never created or consumed, but simply passed from one form to another. One of these forms was called potential energy, or stored energy. When a clock is wound, the energy spent in turning the key is transmitted to, and stored in, the tightly coiled mainspring. The other form of energy is kinetic energy—the energy of motion. A boulder pushed off a cliff and sent crashing into the canyon below has kinetic energy, devastating and murderous, crushing whatever blocks its path.

One of the 19th Century scientists who was convinced that energy was indestructible was the English physicist James Joule. In his most celebrated demonstration Joule used the kinetic energy of a falling weight to turn a miniature paddle wheel. The paddles churned the water and created friction, thus raising the water's temperature. Joule measured the energy delivered to the paddles by the falling weight and then measured the rise in temperature. They were proportional. The kinetic energy had not been lost or dissipated, it had simply been transformed into another form of energy—thermal energy.

Not long after Joule performed his experiments a young German scientist, Hermann von Helmholtz, stated the principle as a law. It is sometimes called, logically enough, the Law of the Conservation of Energy, but it is far better known in the world of modern science as the First Law of Thermodynamics. It says, in effect, that when a gas is heated, the amount of heat added equals the change in the internal energy of the gas, plus the work that the gas does in expanding. Without deliberately seeking it, Helmholtz had chanced upon the last piece of the weather puzzle.

Almost as fast as the theories of Newton, Boyle, Charles, Dalton and

ROBERT BOYLE (1627-1691)

FORMULATORS OF THE LAW of gases, Robert Boyle and Jacques Charles gave meteorology one of its first physical principles. Working 100 years apart, the two men explained the relationships of temperature, volume and pressure in all gases, including air.

JACQUES CHARLES (1746-1823)

Helmholtz appeared, other men began to apply them to the study of the weather. One of the most gifted of these men was Edmund Halley, Britain's Astronomer-Royal from 1720 to 1742. Friend of Newton and financial backer for the publication of his *Principia*, Halley was a dedicated scientist and cataloguer of stars. He discovered the comet that bears his name, and became a student of Arabic languages in order to read the records of ancient astronomers. Halley made numerous contributions to the science of weather, but his greatest one is a celebrated memoir on the cause of tropical trade winds and monsoons, illustrated with history's first meteorological map. Not all of the memoir's contents are original, and some of its assumptions are naive, but it marks a meteorological milestone—a beginning attempt to combine theories about the atmospheric processes with firsthand observation of their results.

Halley based his conclusions partly on his own observations, made at sea and during a two-year stay on the island of St. Helena, and partly on information he collected from globe-girdling mariners. It seemed to him that trade winds and monsoons were caused by the actions of the sun upon the air over the equator. The heated air rose, pulling cooler air in from the south and north. Or, to quote Halley's own words, the movement of the winds was due to "the Action of the Sun's Beams upon the Air and Water, as he passes every day over the Oceans, considered together with the Nature of the Soyl, and the Situation of the adjoyning Continents: I say therefore, first, that according to the Laws of Staticks, the Air, which is less rarified or expanded by heat, and consequently more ponderous, must have a Motion towards those parts thereof, which are more rarified and less ponderous. . . ." Halley's views on this score coincide fairly closely with modern theory. But when he attempted to explain why the trade winds blow from the northeast in the Northern Hemisphere and from the southeast in the Southern Hemisphere, Halley's hypothesis faltered. He could only suggest that they follow "the Sun continually shifting to the Westwards."

The secret of the trade winds

In 1735, some 50 years after the publication of Halley's paper, George Hadley, a London lawyer and philosopher, presented a clearer and much more accurate explanation of the direction of the trade winds. Hadley agreed with Halley that solar radiation and thermal convection accounted for the existence of the trade winds. But the westward movement of the winds was really caused, Hadley said, by the west-to-east rotation of the earth. "The air," said Hadley, "as it moves from the Tropicks towards the Equator, having a less Velocity than the Parts of the earth it arrives at, will have a relative Motion contrary to that of the diurnal Motion of the Earth. . . ."

THE FIRST MAP OF THE WINDS was the work of Edmund Halley, who is best known as an astronomer but who also made the first modern study of the general circulation of the atmosphere. His article, which appeared in 1686 along with the map shown below, described the trade winds and doldrums in the tropics. He correctly attributed them to thermal convection—the rising of tropical air and its distribution outward from the equator.

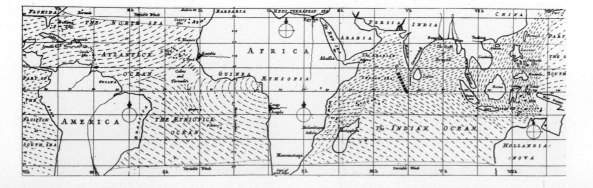

Hadley took account of the fact that the earth's surface is moving faster at the equator than it is north or south of it. In other words, it spins through more miles in one minute at the equator than it does, say, 45° north of the equator. Therefore, reasoned Hadley, a current of air moving toward the equator would lag behind the spinning earth, hitting the equator at a point slightly behind the north-south axis from which it started. Thus it would seem to be moving in a westerly direction. Hadley's reasoning is very close to the currently accepted explanation which assigns the cause to the Coriolis force.

A pirate in a sea of fire

Meanwhile, the day-to-day weather—and storms in particular—was also being closely observed and catalogued by men whose association with it was much more personal. The first description of a typhoon, now a classic of the sea, came from the log of a buccaneer, Captain William Dampier, a contemporary of Halley's. The typhoon caught the pirate captain off the China coast on the afternoon of July 4, 1687, striking from the northeast. Wind howled through the rigging, rain fell in torrential sheets, and toward midnight "it thundered and lightned prodigiously, and the Sea seemed all of a Fire about us: for every Sea that broke sparkled like Lightning."

The eye of the storm passed the next morning "and the Sea tossed us about like an Egg-shell, for want of wind." Shortly after noon on the second day the wind came at Dampier from the opposite point of the compass, the southwest, and the second stage of the typhoon struck the battered vessel. "We presently brail'd up our Mizen, and wore our Ship; but we had no sooner put our Ship before the wind, but it blew a Storm again, and it rain'd very hard; though not so violently as the night before; but the wind was altogether as boysterous, and so continued till 10 or 11 a clock at night. All which time we scudded, or run before the Wind very swift, tho' only with our bare Poles.

"I was never," concludes the captain, "in such a violent Storm in all my life; so said all the Company."

In Philadelphia in 1743, Benjamin Franklin, quite by accident, hit upon the prevailing southwest-to-northeast drift of Atlantic coastal storms. For weeks Franklin had been eagerly looking forward to an eclipse of the moon that was due to occur at 9 p.m. on October 21, but to his intense dismay clouds gathered on that very afternoon. "Before 8," he later noted, "a storm blew up at NE and continued violent all Night and all next Day . . . so that neither Moon nor Stars could be seen."

Several years later, recalling the storm in a letter to a friend, Franklin observed that "what surpriz'd me, was to find in the Boston Newspapers an Account of an Observation of that Eclipse made there: for I had

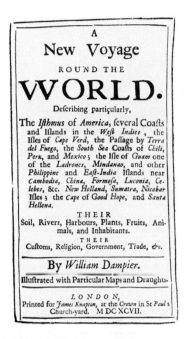

A SCIENTIFIC BUCCANEER, the 17th Century sea captain William Dampier is credited by modern meteorologists with being a pioneer collector of weather data. In 1697, following an eight-year voyage that combined scientific research with piracy, Dampier published the book whose title appears above. In it he described—in detail and for the first time—a China Sea typhoon.

thought, as the Storm came from the NE, it must have begun sooner at Boston than with us, and consequently have prevented such Observation." At the same time he noted that a severe storm had hit Boston on the following day, the 22nd, sweeping high tides across the wharves, smashing small craft and flooding streets along the Boston waterfront.

It must have been, Franklin reasoned, the same storm. And in spite of its northeast surface winds, it must have been traveling from the southwest. "Upon comparing all the other accounts I received from the several colonies, of the time of the beginning of the same storm, and, since that of other storms of the same kind," he wrote later, "I found the beginning to be always later the farther northeastward. I . . . cannot, from memory, say the proportion of time to distance, but I think it is about an hour to every hundred miles."

The hurricane's whirling winds

Nearly 80 years later, similar firsthand observation by an inquisitive Connecticut storekeeper led to meteorology's first accurate description of the wind system of a tropical hurricane. A few weeks after the great September hurricane of 1821 had battered the Atlantic Coast and western New England, storekeeper William C. Redfield traveled across storm-ravaged Connecticut, and noticed a strange thing. In the vicinity of his home in the central part of the state, the hurricane had toppled trees toward the northwest. But 40 or 50 miles to the west, in Litchfield County, the storm had blown down trees in the opposite direction. This could only have been done, he correctly surmised, by a whirlwind.

Several years later, on a boat trip across Long Island Sound, Redfield fell into conversation with Professor Denison Olmsted of Yale. Like many such conversations, this one turned upon the weather, and the two men fell to reminiscing about the hurricane. Redfield's observations fascinated Olmsted, and he encouraged the storekeeper to continue his research. For years after that, Redfield collected data about hurricanes and other violent storms. He pored over ships' logs, interviewed sea captains, collected newspaper clippings.

In 1831, 10 years after his post-hurricane trip across Connecticut, he published a historic meteorological paper, "Remarks on the Prevailing Storms of the Atlantic Coast of the North American States," in the *American Journal of Science and the Arts*. It advanced a remarkable hypothesis, long since confirmed: that a hurricane has a rotary, counter-clockwise wind system with a central eye of calm, and that, although its winds are fierce, its actual progress is slow.

Twelve years later a professional balloonist, John Wise, wrote a harrowing account of his nightmarish experience in the violent convection updrafts of a thunderstorm near Harrisburg, Pennsylvania.

A SUPER-BALLOON for meteorologists, the *Minerva*, dreamed up in 1804 by a French balloonist named Etienne Robertson, was designed to carry 60 meteorologists and astronomers—the pick of the learned societies —on a round-the-world voyage of observation. The balloon was to carry a fully equipped observatory, a study for the scholars, and a banner with a Latin motto meaning "for the sake of knowledge." Not surprisingly, the *Minerva* never got off the drawing board.

"The first sensations," he wrote, "were extremely unpleasant. . . . The cold had now become intense, and everything around me of a fibrous nature became thickly covered with hoarfrost, my whiskers jutting out with it far beyond my face, and the cords running up from my car looking like glass rods, these being glazed with ice and snow, and hail was indiscriminately pelting all around me. . . . I soon found myself whirling upward with a fearful rapidity, the balloon gyrating and the car describing a large circle in the cloud. A noise resembling the rushing of a thousand milldams, intermingled with a dismal moaning sound of wind, surrounded me. . . . The balloon subsided only to be hurled upward again, when, having attained its maximum, it would again sink down with a swinging and fearful velocity, to be carried up again. . . . This happened eight or ten times, all the time the storm raging with unabated fury. . . .

"Once I saw the earth through a chasm in the cloud, but was hurled up once more after that, when, to my great joy, I fell clear out of it, after having been belched up and swallowed down repeatedly by this huge and terrific monster of the air for a space of twenty minutes. . . . I landed, in the midst of a pouring rain, on the farm of Mr. Goodyear, five miles from Carlisle, in a fallow field, where the dashing rain bespattered me with mud from head to foot, as I stood in my car looking up at the fearful element which had just disgorged me."

Looking back on the history of their profession, meteorologists generally consider that its theoretical and practical aspects finally began to merge around 1900 in the work of an extraordinary group of scientists at the Norwegian Geophysical Institute, the Bergen School, led by Vilhelm Bjerknes. By Bjerknes' time, weather data had become more accurate and, thanks to such technological advances as the telegraph, more comprehensive. Bjerknes dared to suggest that day-to-day weather forecasting could be elevated from educated guesswork to an exact science. He first broached the concept in 1904, in a paper entitled, "Weather Forecasting as a Problem in Mechanics and Physics."

A meteorological chessboard

The Bjerknes system was simple and straightforward, with the logical inevitability of an end game in chess. It outlined a meteorological operation that would begin with a data-collecting network, as far-ranging as possible. The network would gather regular readings of temperature, pressure, humidity and wind velocity at the earth's surface and in the upper air. From these data a graph, or map, would be made, showing what Bjerknes called "the initial state of the atmosphere"—the weather as it existed at the time of the readings. Then the data would be translated into mathematical terms, and these would be used—with the help of mathematical equations—to compute the weather to come.

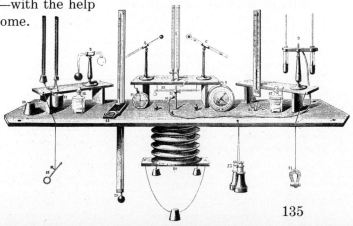

AN INSTRUMENT PANEL for meteorological balloon ascents was invented by the English scientist James Glaisher for use on his first flight in 1862. Its instruments included several thermometers (1,4,5), two barometers (3,7), a compass (13) and opera glasses (23). The panel was attached to the balloon's basket like a table lying across the pilot's knees.

135

Bjerknes worked very hard to put his system into practice, and although the effort never completely succeeded, it did produce some remarkable side effects. During World War I, when Norway was cut off from foreign weather reports, Bjerknes saw that he would need data from more stations, including some on shipboard—and this would cost more money. To get it, he went to the Norwegian fishing-fleet operators and cannily suggested that for the equivalent of a few herring in kroner they could have much more precise weather predictions. The fishermen saw his point and chipped in, and Norway got a world-famous weather service. One consequence of the service was a new meteorological theory. With the intensified coverage that the service provided, the Norwegian scientists were able to confirm a suspected relationship between air masses and the formation of cyclones. The relationship is most closely associated with the name of Bjerknes' son, Jakob, and it is called the "polar-front" theory.

The meetings of the air

According to this theory, a great mass of cold polar air flows generally from east to west in the far northern latitudes. Farther south, in the mid-latitudes, another mass of warmer, moisture-laden air moves from west to east. The front itself—a term analogous to the "front" of a battlefield, where two opposing forces meet—is the surface where the two air masses meet. But the word "front" is slightly misleading. Polar easterlies and mid-latitude westerlies do not confront each other head on; rather, they speed past each other, like trains traveling in opposite directions on adjoining tracks.

Though many other factors may be involved in the formation of a cyclone, it usually starts out as a disturbance in the flow of these two great currents. Any number of things may cause such a disturbance—for example, the interference of a range of mountains, or the difference between sea and land temperatures. Even the slightest disturbance in a region of great temperature contrasts may set off a chain of events resulting in a cyclonic weather movement. Whatever the cause, the consequence is a wavelike undulation in the currents and the fronts that separate them. Sometimes the wave dies out, and a smooth flow is restored. More often, the currents meander back and forth in loops and swirls that ultimately develop into eddies several hundreds of miles across. At this point the cyclone spins off with a peculiar movement of its own.

Today the polar-front theory of the Bergen School seems highly oversimplified. Its air masses and fronts are useful and meaningful in the jargon of meteorologists, and are indispensable in weather maps and forecasts, but the theory itself is outmoded. The Bjerknes name today

A METEOROLOGICAL CHECKERBOARD was part of the dream plan for a numerical weather-forecasting center conceived by Lewis Fry Richardson. He envisaged the world divided up into a checkerboard of 2,000 observing stations, each supplying data. The map above is taken from his book. As Richardson saw it, shaded squares would report barometric pressure while light squares were sending in wind data. Names are points which Richardson knew to be at or near the center of their squares; each square, even at sea, would have a station at its center.

is associated more often with the polar-front theory than with the bold dream of an exact science of weather forecasting. And yet the dream was far more important—even if, despite his valiant efforts, Bjerknes himself did not make it come true. He had the right formulas, the right data and the right idea, but the mathematical technique needed to make the system work remained tantalizingly out of reach.

Even as the Norwegians struggled with their problem, however, a solution was taking shape in the mind of a British mathematician, Lewis Fry Richardson. Richardson thought it might be possible to solve the complex equations that eluded the Norwegians by working them out in step-by-step computations using simple addition, subtraction, multiplication and division. All through World War I, in between ambulance-driving duties, Richardson toiled away at his manuscript. Finally, in 1922, it was printed under the title *Weather Prediction by Numerical Process*. It was a strange and quixotic addition to the literature of science, proving that numerical methods do indeed solve the problem, but it had two drawbacks. To put it into practice, he needed data from upward of 2,000 permanent weather stations around the globe, equipped to collect both surface and upper-air readings. And the numerical processing of this would have required an army of 64,000 mathematicians punching away at 64,000 calculators 24 hours a day, each day of the year.

Richardson must have realized that he was demanding a physical impossibility, for he went on to describe a "forecast factory" that at the time was pure science fiction. It would be a large circular hall, like a theater-in-the-round. The walls would be painted to form a map of the globe, with the North Pole on the ceiling, England in the balcony, the tropics in the dress circle, and Antarctica in the orchestra pit. The 64,000 calculators would be clicking away, each in its assigned position, and electric signs would flash their answers.

An orchestra of weathermen

From a raised pulpit in the center, the supervisor and his staff would control the whole operation. One of his duties would be to see that no part of the world fell behind in its calculations. "In this respect," wrote Richardson, "he is like the conductor of an orchestra in which the instruments are slide-rules and calculating machines." As fast as the predictions were computed, pneumatic tubes would whisk them to a remote room for coding and relaying to a radio transmitting station.

Incredibly, less than 25 years later it all began to come true. Speeded by World War II technology, the centuries-long evolution of the calculating machine finally produced a contraption that could do the work not of merely 64,000 mathematicians, but of 100,000. One of the first of these electronic computers was Von Neumann's MANIAC.

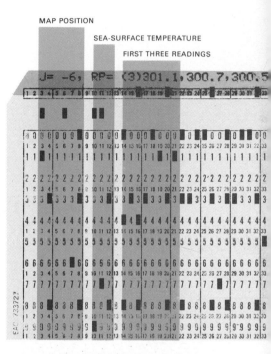

A TICKET TO A FORECAST, the IBM card above is what enables a computer to turn weather data into a prediction. The gray horizontal band at top starts at left with a code (J = −6) indicating where the data were collected. A second code (RP=) indicates readings representing sea-surface temperature. The readings themselves follow. These data, punched on a series of four cards, tell the computer the sea temperature every 310 miles along a line stretching from the central Pacific to the northeast coast of Africa.

This machine seemed the perfect solution to the crushing mechanical difficulties so appealingly, and so hopelessly, presented by Richardson in his *Weather Prediction by Numerical Process*. Accordingly, in 1946, Von Neumann began to assemble at Princeton a group of young, creative and highly talented meteorologists and mathematicians.

For the next 10 years, these and other top scientists in the field toiled at the trailblazing task of reducing the intricacies of meteorology to a form that could be digested by a high-speed computer. They diagnosed the errors of Richardson's calculations, worked out formulations of existing equations, solved previously unassailable problems and analyzed far more new data than Richardson could ever have dreamed of.

Von Neumann's scientists had at their disposal a vast network of weather stations, which were feeding in information from 100 million cubic miles of space, and modern weather balloons carrying the latest electronic sensing and transmitting equipment . By 1956, Von Neumann's team had finally and firmly established the foundation for a new and far more sophisticated meteorology: the analysis and prediction of weather by mathematics and machine.

"Perhaps some day in the dim future," Richardson had written, "it will be possible to advance the computations faster than the weather advances." That "dim future" had arrived.

Myths, Deities and Computers

The study of weather began as myth. To early man, weather was a divinely ordered phenomenon, and tribal priests related storms and fair weather to the mood of the gods. In the Fifth Century B.C., Greek philosophers first began to suspect that there were natural causes behind the weather. But lacking instruments and an understanding of the laws of physics, they could only speculate. Slowly, however, the tools for measuring weather became available. At the same time, such brilliant scientists as Newton and Boyle were formulating the physical laws essential to the study of weather. It was not until the early 1900s, when meteorology finally came into its own, that the complexity of this new branch of science began to be realized. Today, meteorological computations are being handled by computers—which have demonstrated, among other things, that inherent in the subject are problems that will stump computers as yet undesigned.

A MEDIEVAL GUIDE TO THE WINDS
Man as microcosm is subject to the winds of the greater world in this medieval miniature. The fire, water, earth and air, of which man and universe were thought to be composed, are portrayed affecting the nature both of the winds and of man. Each wind has its own character. The east wind *(top)* is "drying" and "temperate," while the west wind *(bottom)* "dispels winter, produces flowers."

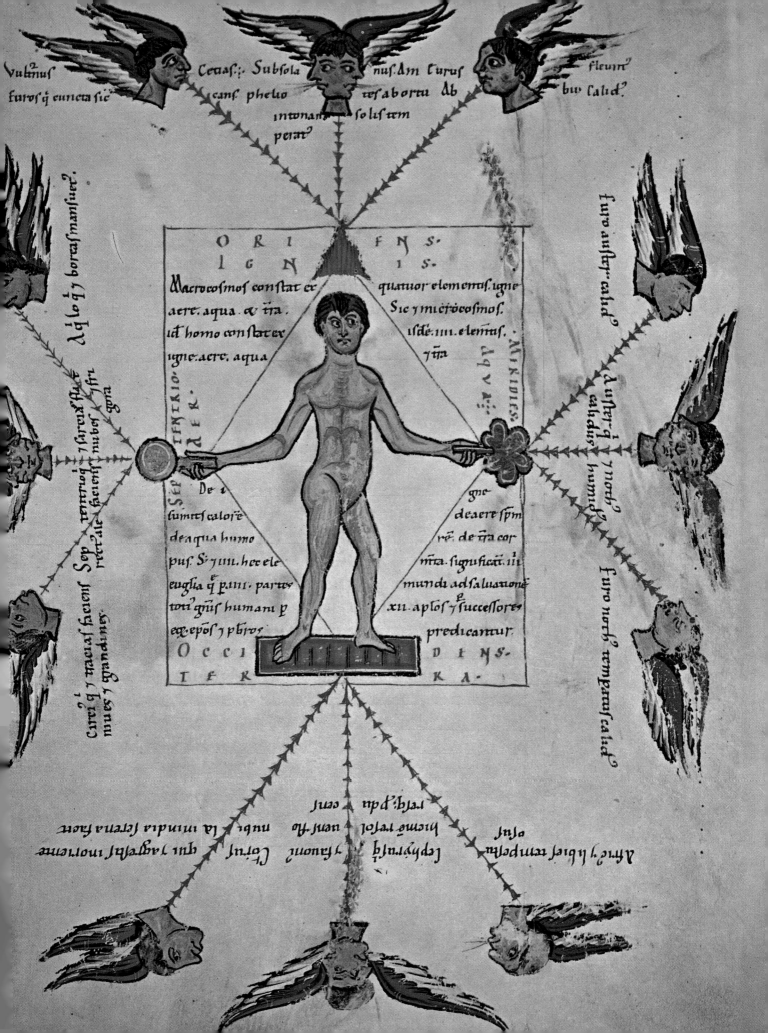

A PAIR OF ORIENTAL DEITIES

Riding a cloud, two Chinese weather gods, dating from very ancient times, herald the approach of a thunderstorm. The one at left, Lei Chen Tzu, bringer of lightning, wears a halo of fire symbolizing his power. The drum at his side produces thunder, and his ax splits trees. Fei Lien, the god of wind with a dragon's body, needs no such equipment—only his lungs.

The Stormy Moods
of Ancient Gods

In man's earliest attempts to explain the weather, he personified its various elements and imbued them with human traits. The most common of these was anger, and the figures most often portrayed were those representing violent storms, such as the two ancient Chinese gods at left. Similarly, the Norsemen had a whole assortment of gods whose moods were said to account for the weather; Thor was the most famous—a paradoxical figure who brought both beneficial rain and terrible storms, and produced lightning with a red-hot hammer held in an iron glove.

The mythology of meteorology achieved its most detailed exposition under the Greeks and Romans (below). The Greeks had many weather gods, including Iris, in charge of creating rainbows, and Eos, goddess of the dawn, whose tears shed at sunrise sprinkled the earth with dew.

THE BRINGERS OF WIND
This Fifth Century miniature shows rival Greek deities battling over the Trojan fleet, as told in Vergil's *Aeneid.* Two horned gods of wind, in the corners, are blowing up a dangerous storm.

But Neptune, god of the sea (called Poseidon by the Greeks), appears above the waves. Angered by the invasion of his domain by the wind gods, he brandishes his trident and banishes them.

Tools for a Science

The word "meteorology" traces its origins at least to the Fourth Century B.C., when Aristotle wrote a work on weather and called it *Meteorologica* (literally, "discourses on the atmosphere"). But it was not until about 400 years ago that the basic instruments began to evolve that were required to turn the study of weather into the science of meteorology.

The brilliant experimenter Galileo, seeking a way to measure temperature changes, contributed the thermometer about 1600. Fifty years later, Galileo's protégé, Evangelista Torricelli, developed the barometer *(right)*. There followed, in 1780, Horace Bénédict de Saussure's simple hair hygrometer *(opposite, below)* for measuring humidity. And rain gauges and weather vanes, known since antiquity, were constantly improved by men like Britain's master architect, Sir Christopher Wren.

By 1790 the basic assortment of instruments—the tool kit that has served the standard surface weather observatory ever since—was complete.

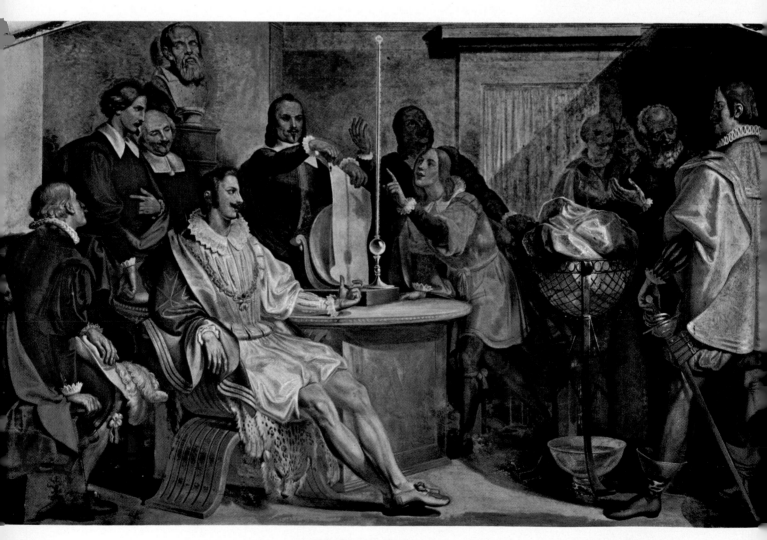

A CONCEPT OF COLD
Members of Florence's Accademia del Cimento (the words mean "experimental academy"), using a basket of ice, a mirror and a thermometer, perform an experiment for Grand Duke Ferdinand, to see if cold can be reflected like heat. The answer: it cannot, because while heat is a form of energy, cold is merely the absence of heat. The academy existed from 1657 to 1667.

A DIAGONAL BAROMETER

An improved version of Torricelli's instrument, this 1753 barometer has the upper portion of the mercury column inclined almost to the horizontal. In this position, changes in pressure are easier to read because the mercury moves a greater distance for every change in pressure.

HUMIDITY BY A HAIR

This 1780 hair hygrometer, first of its kind, invented by Horace Bénédict de Saussure, makes use of the moisture absorbency of human hair to measure atmospheric humidity. The pointer at the bottom registers changes in the hair as it lengthens in wet weather and contracts in dry.

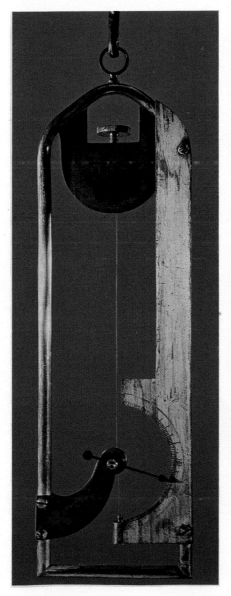

WEATHER IN THE WIND

This wind vane, which was recently discovered in an ancient storage room in Florence, registers wind direction on a round dial. Wind vanes are among the earliest known weather tools, dating back to long before the Christian Era. Rooftops in ancient Rome sported wind vanes, showing that even at this early date the relationship between wind and weather was apparent.

A Century of Weather Ballooning

Ballooning, begun in the 18th Century as a sport, turned out to be much more than that for meteorologists. Since 1648, when Pascal and Périer took a barometer up a mountain to show that higher altitude resulted in lower atmospheric pressure, scientists had known that the air's characteristics change with height. But apart from climbing mountains and flying kites, they could not get instruments high enough to make studies.

The breakthrough came in France in 1783, when the Montgolfier brothers invented the hot-air balloon. Their efforts were followed by flights by the physicist Jacques Charles, who took a barometer along to show altitude. This was an aeronautical rather than a meteorological use for the instrument, but two years later Dr. John Jeffries (right) made the first scientific measurements of temperature, humidity and barometric pressure at heights up to 9,000 feet.

Numerous meteorological ascents followed, many of them risky. The last of the scientific balloon pioneers, James Glaisher, made 28 flights between 1862 and 1866. Testing the composition of the air at 29,000 feet, he was almost asphyxiated (opposite).

WINDS ACROSS THE CHANNEL
Plotting wind direction, physician John Jeffries rides with French balloonist Jean Pierre Blanchard. The two had to strip to their underwear to reduce weight and keep the leaky craft aloft.

A FLIGHT FOR SCIENCE
Cheered by an excited crowd of Parisians, the balloon designed by physicist Jacques Charles returns triumphantly from its flight in December 1783. Charles, who later formulated the gas laws which helped explain the behavior of the atmosphere, took a barometer on this flight so he could tell his altitude by measuring the drop in pressure as the balloon gained height.

RUNNING OUT OF AIR

British scientist James Glaisher sprawls unconscious from lack of oxygen while his pilot, arms half-paralyzed by cold, opens a control valve with his teeth. Glaisher fainted at 29,000 feet, after recording a barometer reading of 9.75 inches. Both men survived the 1862 flight.

A PROFILE OF THE WEATHER

This map charts the weather encountered by James Glaisher on June 26, 1863, during one of his 28 balloon ascents. In a 50-mile flight, lasting an hour and a half, he ran into rain, snow and fog—plus temperatures ranging from "extreme heat of summer" to "cold of winter."

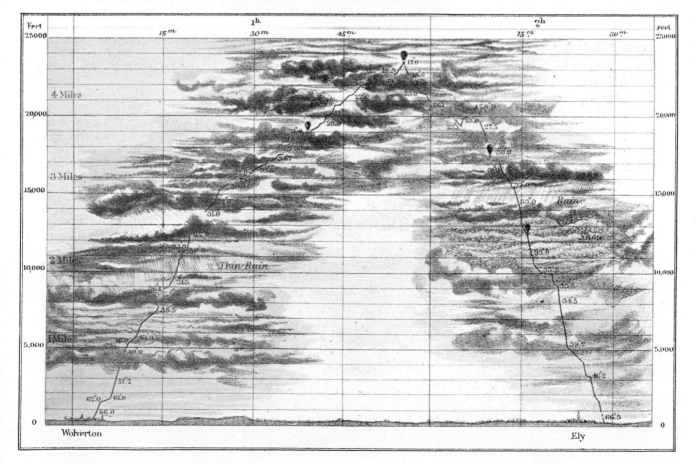

DISASTER AT BALAKLAVA
French and English warships founder off Balaklava during a violent storm which caught the Allied fleet by surprise on November 14, 1854. Investigation proved the disaster could have been averted had news of the coming storm been transmitted by wire to the Black Sea port.

DATA BY TELEGRAPH
Operators in the Paris telegraph office *(left)* receive observational data for relay to the French national weather bureau, founded in 1856 as a direct result of the Balaklava disaster *(above)*. By 1863, France was regularly publishing a map which showed the European weather picture.

WIRES FOR WEATHER
The U.S. communications link vital to forecasting moves westward as linemen string telegraph wires across the Great Plains in the 1860s. Meantime, Dr. Joseph Henry of the Smithsonian Institution had begun issuing daily weather maps based on data received by telegraph.

Telegraphy Supplies the Missing Link

As the 19th Century dawned, the instruments were at hand to allow accurate weather observations. But as the essayist John Ruskin pointed out, "the meteorologist is impotent if alone"—i.e., observations are no use unless rapidly communicated. By mid-century the telegraph provided a way to bring together swiftly the observations on which forecasts are based, but at first little was done to put the device to use. Then, during the Crimean War, a hurricane caught the Allied fleet by surprise *(left)*, and almost cost France and England the war. Two years later, at France's instigation, the world's first telegraphic weather network was set up.

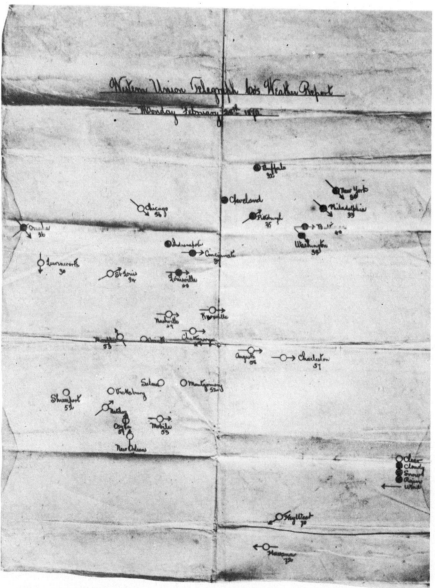

AN EARLY WEATHER MAP
One of the earliest weather maps in the U.S., compiled at the Cincinnati Weather Observatory for February 28, 1870, from data received by telegraph, indicates the weather at 31 different stations in the east-central U.S. The notations also show temperature and wind direction. Some months later, the National Weather Service was started under the Army Signal Corps.

Discovering
the Grand Design

By the early 1900s, meteorologists knew that the key to accurate forecasting lay in collecting ample data: reports from a sufficient number of widely scattered observers would enable them to see further into the future patterns of local weather.

Scientists knew that the weather in one place was part of a huge meteorological fabric that covered the whole globe. But the mechanism which controlled all this was a mystery. However, in Bergen, Norway, a slim man named Vilhelm Bjerknes was formulating a theory that would go far to explain it. Starting with a strong hunch that some sort of general pattern for the weather would emerge

from sufficient data, Bjerknes persuaded the Norwegian Government to help set up strategically located observing stations. In addition, Bjerknes founded a school which attracted meteorologists from all over the world, including Carl-Gustaf Rossby *(opposite)*, who later pioneered the study of the upper atmosphere.

Bjerknes' own son Jakob, himself a student at the school, was also destined to make meteorological history. Building on his father's ideas, Jakob, with a colleague, developed the revolutionary polar-front theory, which explains a great deal about the global origins of everyday weather. A grand design was beginning to emerge.

A FORMULATOR OF THEORIES
Norway's Vilhelm Bjerknes, founder of the Bergen School of Meteorology, wears a self-effacing smile and a chestful of medals in this 1948 picture, taken three years before his death.

BIRTHPLACE OF A REVOLUTION
In 1919 members of the Bergen Weather Service plot weather maps from observations received by telegraph. Their forecasts were sent mainly to farmers and fishermen. It was largely from studies made in this room that the polar-front theory emerged. Two pioneers appear in this picture: Carl-Gustaf Rossby, at the center of the table, and Jakob Bjerknes, standing at rear.

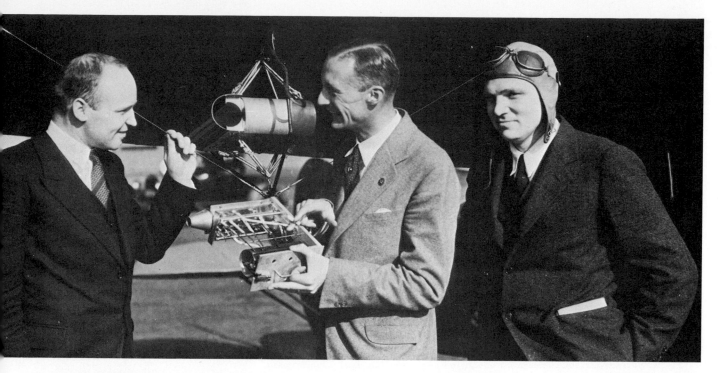

A FLIGHT FOR FACTS

Carl-Gustaf Rossby *(left)*, early advocate of upper-air research, discusses a new device, the meteorograph, held by Karl Lange. The instrument recorded weather data at various heights; it was later carried to 19,000 feet on an airplane piloted by scientist Daniel Sayre *(right)*.

A SUPPLEMENTAL SEARCH

M.I.T. pilot-engineer Henry Harris peers from the cabin of a research plane used in connection with the balloon flights at the right. While the meteorograph-bearing balloons were recording vital statistics of the atmosphere, Harris took supplemental readings from his plane.

BALLOONS INTO THE STRATOSPHERE

Carl-Gustaf Rossby *(right foreground)* helps hold a meteorograph-equipped balloon at Lambert Field, St. Louis, in 1934. The meteorograph automatically recorded atmospheric pressure, temperature and humidity. At about 65,000 feet the balloon burst and floated back to earth, still bearing the instrument. Finders were paid five dollars to return the devices to Rossby.

A Machine
for Meteorology

A meteorologist's dream came true in the late 1940s in the form of the electronic computer, capable of digesting bushels of facts and spewing out answers—precisely the tool weathermen had needed for years. A group of meteorologists, hearing that Dr. John Von Neumann was designing a computer, proposed that it be tried in forecasting. The idea intrigued Von Neumann. He and his colleagues began work on equations (which reduced the weather to a sort of formula) to be fed to the computer.

The first test, in 1950, was remarkably successful. But later trials produced wildly fictional weather (e.g., a July blizzard in Georgia)—confirming that a computer forecast was only as perfect as the equations fed into the machine. Scientists have been trying to perfect the equations ever since.

A COMPUTER AND ITS DESIGNER
Finished with the six-year job of developing the first computer for weather research, mathematician John Von Neumann displays his machine at Princeton, New Jersey. Von Neumann called the machine MANIAC—for Mathematical Analyzer, Numerical Integrator and Computer.

A VICTORY PORTRAIT
After running the first successful computer forecast in 1950, Von Neumann *(second from left)* and two Princeton colleagues, Dr. Ragnar Fjörtoft *(third from right)* and Dr. Jule Charney *(right)*, are shown with U.S. Weather Bureau meteorologists at Aberdeen, Maryland. In this first trial run, made on a borrowed computer, Von Neumann and members of his Princeton team proved that a computer could actually make a forecast as well as skilled weathermen.

BOUND FOR THE UPPER AIR
Ready to transmit a stream of temperature, humidity and pressure data from the upper air, a radiosonde balloon is released from Tatoosh Island, Washington. Balloons such as this supply much data for Weather Bureau computers.

THE U.S. WEATHER BUREAU'S National Meteorological Center (NMC) in Suitland, Maryland, the largest weather-computing center in the world, is, in effect, the forecast factory that Lewis Fry Richardson dreamed of and that John Von Neumann did so much to bring to fruition. Here, four times a day, an enormous complex of computers devours millions of bits of weather data from thousands of observing stations all over the Northern Hemisphere, hums through millions upon millions of calculations, and within 90 minutes or so starts flashing coded numerical weather analyses and forecasts by Teletype to hundreds of Weather Bureau and military offices throughout the United States and lands overseas.

At the NMC, not even the weather maps are drawn by human hand. Automatic curve-plotters integrated with the computers sketch out maps of weather and winds over the Northern Hemisphere as they were a few hours ago; throughout the far-flung network of recipient stations, the maps simultaneously appear as if by magic on electrolytic facsimile printers. Thanks to electronics, the NMC can send such a volume of information to each station that the weatherman on the spot can make a local prediction without so much as a glance out the window.

Still, not even an organization as big as the NMC is big enough for the meteorologist to reach his elusive goal: the perfect forecast every day of the year. Which way the weather will go depends on many factors; one expert has suggested only half-facetiously that the guesswork will not begin to be removed from prediction until there is a weather-reporting station for every two square inches of the earth's surface. Meanwhile, as the late English meteorologist and author, Sir Napier Shaw, once wrote, "A forecaster's heart knoweth its own bitterness, and a stranger meddleth not with its joy." The weather still flirts with the forecaster and makes a fool of him, but if he outguesses it he can congratulate himself on his own shrewdness and learning. And as he looks back to the past, he cannot help but take satisfaction in how far his professional art has come from where it started.

For many centuries men believed that weather changed at the whim of the gods. Bad weather, in fact, was one of the principal ways in which the gods toyed with man. Writing in about the Eighth Century B.C., Homer describes how Poseidon, god of the sea, seeing Odysseus adrift on his raft, "gathered the clouds and troubled the waters of the deep . . . and he roused all storms of all manner of winds, and shrouded in clouds the land and sea."

But even while the Greeks were attributing weather to the whims of the gods, they were also studying weather as a phenomenon subject to natural laws. By the Fifth Century B.C. they were publicly posting weather observations—wind data for the most part—for the use of mariners. In the Fourth Century B.C. Aristotle wrote his monumental study

A COMPUTER'S ROSE
This flowerlike picture is actually an early type of numerical forecast predicting some of the next day's weather elements—such as pressure force and wind speed—for the Northern Hemisphere. Such forecasts are read by meteorologists like a map, with the center representing the North Pole. The patterns are produced by the computer from hundreds of observations.

A WHEEL BAROMETER, designed in 1666 to permit more accurate readings of the changes in a standard tube of mercury, was invented by Robert Hooke, one of the most ingenious mechanical innovators of his age. A small float, riding on the column of mercury, was connected by a string to a pulley which moved a pointer, thus making it possible to observe relatively minute changes in barometric pressure.

of the physics of the earth and air, *Meteorologica*. But weather prediction was still necessarily a matter of reading natural signs in advance. The most industrious compiler of this classical weather lore was Aristotle's pupil Theophrastus. His *Book of Signs*, written about 300 B.C., described more than 200 portents of rain, wind and fair weather, and a few that were alleged to reveal what the weather would be like for the coming year or more. He described signs to be found in the behavior of sheep, the way a lamp burns during a storm and the crawling of centipedes toward a wall. His book was a major reference work for forecasting for the next 2,000 years.

The myth of the flies

Many of the curiosities that still linger in popular weather lore can be traced right back to Theophrastus—for example, the myth that flies bite excessively before a storm. In fact, flies bite equally hard and often in any weather. On the other hand, some of Theophrastus' observations have been made many times, under many skies, and have remained current for good reason. Theophrastus noted that a red sunrise and a halo around the sun or moon are all portents of rain, while a red sunset is a portent of good weather. All have been shown by one modern meteorological study to be accurate at least seven times out of 10.

But on the whole, ancient weather wisdom was a sketchy and highly subjective guide for forecasting. The scientific study of weather had to wait until the 17th Century and the development of instruments for quantitative measurements. In the 25 centuries since the time of ancient Greece, men had commonly used tools to measure only two elements of weather: rainfall and wind direction. They used a bucket and ruler to find the first, and weather vanes to find the second. When more instruments finally came, they came swiftly, sweeping away within the century the dominion of Aristotle, Theophrastus and old shepherds' tales.

First to be used for prediction was the barometer, invented by Torricelli in 1643. Renaissance scientists were soon fascinated to observe that certain kinds of weather often accompanied certain pressure readings. The barometer came to be called the "weather glass," and was believed for a time to be a foolproof weather prophet. When Robert Hooke devised a wheel barometer, with a pointer and dial to indicate the rise and fall of the mercury, predictions were made part of the barometer itself— and can still be seen on some barometers: "Change" at 29.5 inches of pressure, flanked by "Rain" and "Stormy" at lower pressures, and "Fair" and "Very Dry" at higher pressures. Some barometers bore 10 different weather descriptions at different pressure readings.

Actually, atmospheric pressure depends on many factors, including altitude, and is a far from certain indicator of a specific kind of weather.

A barometer's chief usefulness to forecasting today is to indicate that change itself is on the way, for a change in pressure does indeed usually herald a change in weather. But exactly what *kind* of weather will arrive can be foretold only with much more information than the barometer alone supplies.

Along with the barometer came the thermometer and Robert Hooke's "hygroscope" for measuring humidity. Armed with these instruments, the enthusiastic scientists of the 17th Century began laying the basis for a real understanding of weather: the keeping of careful records. Scientific observation had to precede scientific prediction. Over the next 200 years, the first modern meteorologists built up a storehouse of recorded measurements, not only in order to learn more about the physics of weather, but also to discover its movement and patterns, so that predictions might be made on the basis of the past.

Records still exist of simultaneous observations made between 1649 and 1651 in two French cities—Paris and Clermont-Ferrand—and in Stockholm, Sweden. The records, delivered by a primitive postal service, arrived at the collection point days or weeks behind the atmospheric conditions they described. By the end of the century, regular records, both local and international, were being kept by such diverse parties as Central European grand dukes, England's Royal Society, and the city of Charleston, South Carolina. Information passed from scientist to scientist, and from country to country, giving meteorology the cooperative, international character that distinguishes it to this day.

A statesmanlike interest in weather

Many of the great men of the 18th Century interested themselves in weather just as they interested themselves in other momentous affairs of the time. Benjamin Franklin's contribution to meteorology was conspicuous, but George Washington, Thomas Jefferson, James Madison and John Quincy Adams all kept weather records. (In Philadelphia on the morning of July 4, 1776, the day the Declaration of Independence was adopted, Jefferson recorded the temperature at 6 a.m. at 68°F.) Boston's weather records were kept jointly by a Harvard professor and the Chief Justice of Massachusetts.

Eventually, weather records were being kept throughout the civilized world. In the early 1800s, U.S. Army hospital surgeons were ordered to take regular observations—thus beginning the first meteorological service financed by the U.S. Government. By 1853 weather records were being filed daily in 97 different Army camps.

As data became more abundant, instruments more accurate and observational techniques more uniform, students of weather gained an ever-clearer picture of its passage over large areas. By the 19th Century,

A HAYLOFT HYGROMETER, made of rope and a stick, is a homemade instrument for forecasting bad weather. When the air's humidity increases, the rope absorbs moisture. Its strands lengthen and unwind slightly, moving the stick in a circle. When the humidity drops, the rope winds up again, reversing the stick. Crude but fairly accurate, this rustic instrument was based on an old farmers' saying: "When the ropes twist, forget your haying."

meteorologists had ample confirmation of one of the central precepts of forecasting: that weather develops progressively as the atmosphere flows across the face of the land. Weather maps drawn in the 1840s by James Espy and Yale University's Elias Loomis established the generally west-to-east progress of cyclonic storms. But this knowledge of weather's broad movements was of no practical use as long as weather news could be sent no faster than stagecoach or ship could carry it. The charts the theorists patiently constructed showed weather long since past, weather that had already lost its significance for the present, let alone the future.

A miracle of communication

Samuel F. B. Morse's electromagnetic telegraph finally wrought the miracle of rapid communication—and revolutionized meteorology as dramatically as had the thermometer and barometer some 200 years before. The first telegraph lines were built between Washington, D.C. and Baltimore in 1844. The implications for meteorology were immediately grasped by Joseph Henry, an inventor of an earlier telegraphic device himself, and now secretary of the recently founded Smithsonian Institution in Washington. In 1849—almost as fast as telegraph wires were going up—Henry began making a series of agreements with telegraph companies whereby the Smithsonian provided meteorological instruments, and operators telegraphed weather data to the Smithsonian in return.

By the end of the year, operators in dozens of stations were under orders to give weather data top priority, and opened shop each morning by tapping out coded pressure and temperature readings and other weather information. Soon the Smithsonian was publishing daily weather maps of the area encompassed by the network—among the first based on telegraphed data. They were not forecasts, but astute interpreters knew that a storm located over Cincinnati on today's map might well hit Washington tomorrow. By 1860 and the outbreak of the Civil War, upward of 500 telegraph stations were making the wires hum with national weather information for Professor Henry.

Other nations were as quick to exploit the telegraph, and were even quicker to move from collecting current data to forecasting. The French were the first to establish a national storm-warning service, begun in 1856 after the disastrous loss of French and British naval vessels in the Crimean harbor of Balaklava in a storm *(page 146)*. The British launched a similar service in 1860, after a steam clipper was wrecked on the coast of Wales in a gale, with a loss of 450 lives. American progress toward forecasting, however, was seriously interrupted by the Civil War. The war broke the links of Henry's chain of telegraph stations serving the

Smithsonian, and he was never able to reestablish it on such a large scale again.

Organized weather forecasting in the United States was begun not in Washington but in the Midwest, and not by the Government but by one man, the director of the Cincinnati Observatory, Cleveland Abbe. Abbe persuaded both the Cincinnati Chamber of Commerce and the Western Union Telegraph Company of the practicality of local predictions, and with their backing began issuing regular forecasts, which he called "probabilities," on September 1, 1869. He said prophetically at the time, "I have started that which the country will not willingly let die." He received bulletins from only two telegraph operators that first day, but he issued his probability nevertheless—predicting easterly and southeasterly winds. By the end of the year he had a small network of 33 observers telegraphing information.

The next year, in response to mounting pressure from Great Lakes shippers for storm warnings, the U.S. Congress at last appropriated money for a Government-sponsored forecasting agency, placing it under the control of the U.S. Army Signal Service. Its first forecast was issued on November 8, 1870, by Increase Lapham, a Wisconsin scientist. It was based on telegraphic reports from 25 stations, most of them in the Midwest, and was distributed in the Great Lakes area. The forecast read, "High winds probably along the Lakes."

From this beginning, with its pitifully inadequate network of 25 primitively equipped stations, 233 full-time employees and an annual budget of $50,000, has grown what may well be the most complicated and far-flung peacetime organization in history. The modern United States Weather Bureau, operating within the Environmental Science Services Administration (ESSA) of the Department of Commerce, now has under its jurisdiction approximately 300 surface weather observation stations, some 145 upper-air sounding stations on land and at sea and nearly 100 radar weather surveillance stations. Its number of full-time employees has multiplied more than 20 times to nearly 5,000, and its annual appropriation is somewhat over $70 million. As one measure of the usefulness of its work, every year Americans make approximately 250 million telephone calls to get tape-recorded forecasts of tomorrow's weather.

A formidable mosaic

The task of the Weather Bureau is staggering to contemplate. In brief, it is to observe and analyze more than two billion cubic miles of atmosphere that envelops the Northern Hemisphere in a shifting mosaic of weather—a mosaic so complex the Bureau once estimated that the U.S. alone may be covered by 10,000 varieties of weather at once, each significant enough to be of local concern.

CABALISTIC SIGNS, similar to those devised by medieval astronomers, were borrowed in the 18th Century by the Swiss-German scientist Johann Heinrich Lambert, who used them in a weather book published in 1758. Signs such as these came into widespread use in the 18th Century as methods of gathering and exchanging weather observations were increasingly refined by individual scientists and learned societies. They were the precursors of modern meteorological symbols.

CHANGEABLE   SUNSHINE WITH CLOUDS   VERY BRIGHT   FOGGY   LIGHT RAIN   HEAVY RAIN   SNOW

The national, international, public and private resources used by the Bureau to accomplish its task are almost equally awesome. Throughout the Northern Hemisphere, some 2,000 stations of many nations regularly transmit weather data to national or regional collecting centers four times a day, seven days a week. About 500 of them are in the area of most immediate concern to the U.S.: the continent of North America and the surrounding seas. Another 1,500 are land-based stations around the world: stations in Red China, Siberia, the Sahara; in the mists of the Scottish highlands, or in the tropical warmth of Hawaii. Such is the international etiquette of weather-collecting that in all of these places the weathermen on duty perform much the same daily ritual. At midnight, 6 a.m., noon and 6 p.m. Greenwich time, they emerge like the shepherds of old, look at the clouds and note whether the air is hazy. Being modern weathermen, they also read their barometers, thermometers, rain and wind gauges and hygrometers. By radio they transmit the data thus obtained to their headquarters. Perhaps half a world away, the receivers at the NMC pick up the vast body of information, teletypewriters code it on tape and get it ready for the computers' next meal.

Weather reports from sea and sky

On an average day the NMC also picks up some 3,200 ship reports on weather throughout the seven seas, nearly 1,000 reports from commercial aircraft in flight, and at least 200 reports from scheduled reconnaissance flights by military aircraft.

In addition, more than 500 stations in the Northern Hemisphere report on the direction and speed of the great rivers of wind streaming through the stratosphere and troposphere. Twice a day, and sometimes four times a day, radiosonde balloons are sent into the skies over 100 North American stations. They climb at 1,000 feet a minute, their delicate sensors reading temperature, pressure and humidity as they soar upward, their tiny radios flashing the data earthward, until the balloons burst at altitudes of 60,000 or 70,000 feet. All these data, too, converge on the teletypewriter banks at the NMC, and are fed into a battery of computers.

According to a recent publication of the Bureau, one purpose of this vast human and technical endeavor is "to determine and record the . . . climatology on the North American continent and adjacent waters." Another is the discovery of "natural laws governing atmospheric phenomena." But the Weather Bureau's first and foremost function is to forecast weather—to tell a waiting public what kind of day it will be tomorrow and the day after.

Each year the Weather Bureau turns out about 1.2 million general weather forecasts and 750,000 aviation forecasts. It issues 100,000 river-stage and flood forecasts, and additional thousands of special warnings and bulletins regarding tornadoes, hurricanes, hail, lightning, high winds, blizzards, cold waves, fog and frost. Its services are probably used every day by more Americans than those of any other single Government agency except the U.S. Post Office.

The Bureau's short-range forecasts covering the next 18 to 36 hours, issued locally four times a day across the country, influence the life of the nation in all its phases. The real-estate tract operator with a model home to show on Sunday, the bride who wants an outdoor reception, the garageman ordering his antifreeze supply, all these and millions more are vitally interested in tomorrow's weather. They listen with various degrees of feeling to what their local Weather Bureau forecaster has to say about it. One housewife living near the Connecticut shore regularly checks her local station for cloud-cover and ceiling-height forecasts before starting her laundry. She explained to a puzzled weatherman, "When the ceiling is low, the sea gulls fly right over my backyard, and it's no time to hang out laundry. When the ceiling is high they fly another route."

The money the American public saves through this glimpse of the weather ahead is incalculable. The glib estimate is a billion dollars a year, but responsible meteorologists place it much higher, and not only in terms of dollars. Current Weather Bureau figures, for example, indicate that its storm warnings alone not only prevent some $255 million in property damage each year, but also save some 2,600 lives.

Jokes about the Weather Bureau's inaccuracy are, roughly, a generation out of date. There is disagreement over how the accuracy of a prediction is measured, but according to Weather Bureau calculations, accuracy reached a relatively high point in the 1940s, when World War II led to an intensification of effort and new techniques. The percentage of accurate forecasts then leveled off for roughly the next 10 years. Figures varied slightly for different sections of the country, but during this period Bureau forecasts for 12 to 18 hours in advance were about 80 per cent accurate in most areas. Forecasts for 24 to 36 hours in advance were about 70 per cent accurate.

A boost from computers

When the Weather Bureau first began using computer technology in 1955, an improvement in accuracy, "slight but significant," was noted almost immediately. Today 12- to 18-hour forecasts are considered 85 per cent accurate; forecasts up to 36 hours in advance are correct about 75 per cent of the time. Though general weather conditions for about a week in advance can be forecast with some degree of usefulness, it is still beyond the capabilities of science to make detailed predictions for more than about three days in advance.

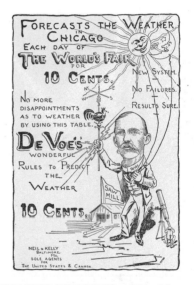

WEATHER WIZARDRY, published for the Chicago World's Fair in 1893, forecasts the weather for all 183 days of the exposition. Its bold author based his "rules" on the notion that weather remains stationary while the earth moves under it, according to a predetermined pattern. Thus, he believed that Chicago would have the same weather in June that had occurred at the equator the previous December.

The achievement of more accurate forecasts, particularly for relatively extended periods, would be of incalculable value to Americans. President Johnson has estimated that if weather could be accurately predicted only five days in advance, Government and industry would save an additional six billion dollars annually in better water-resources management, and lower costs in agriculture, surface transportation, retail marketing and lumbering alone.

With such an enormous commercial incentive, accuracy can and will improve. Better reporting of weather over vacant land areas and oceans is now a major objective of the U.N.'s 126-member World Meteorological Organization. Scientists the world over are seeking a better understanding of the atmosphere, improved techniques for handling masses of statistics, more elaborate computers. All these lines of inquiry will help make tomorrow's weather more predictable.

Such is the pace of technology that it is not hard to imagine a day when every weather prediction is as accurate as it needs to be for the most efficient human planning. Yet even in such a brave new world, weather will still have its unique charm. It is one thing to hear temperature, pressure and humidity predicted with utmost precision over the radio, and another to step outside and find them arrived. A fine day is always a happy surprise.

The Home Weatherman

Meteorology is among the most complex of the physical sciences. In its effort to predict what tomorrow's weather will be, the U.S. Weather Bureau employs some 5,000 people, has an annual budget in excess of $70 million, utilizes one of the most complicated computers ever built and has access to the weather data collected by more than 100 nations. Yet many Americans are discovering that they can do remarkably well at predicting the weather using only a few dollars' worth of equipment. These parlor meteorologists are often surprisingly youthful. John Sims (opposite) was only 13 when he built his own weather station, entered it in a national science contest and won a prize. His forecasting score was far from perfect, but the judges took into account the special handicaps that only an amateur weatherman must cope with—such as the fact that when a west wind blows, John's wind readings are affected by a neighbor's hedge.

A DO-IT-YOURSELF METEOROLOGIST

Entering observations on a weather chart, John Sims stands beside his backyard weather station in Flushing, New York. The station's equipment includes *(from left)* an anemometer for measuring wind speed, a wind-direction indicator, and a shelter housing instruments for recording temperature and humidity. Except for thermometers, all were built from material available at home.

Testing the Air for Moisture

As a deductive process, weather forecasting, whether professional or amateur, bears a close resemblance to medical diagnosis. The weatherman, like the doctor, looks for symptoms in the present weather and makes a prognosis. Like a doctor, he begins by taking the temperature. Then *(below)* he obtains the relative humidity —the amount of water vapor in the air divided by the amount it could hold at a given temperature and pressure. The instruments John Sims uses for this purpose, the psychrometer and hair hygrometer, are explained and pictured in detail at right.

Temperature, in combination with relative humidity, may be a key symptom of coming rain: warm air holds more moisture than cold. If John's instruments show a sharp rise in moisture while temperature remains the same, or conversely if there is a sharp drop in temperature while the moisture holds steady, he knows that the prognosis is possible rain. To set a working figure for relative humidity, he uses the chart at lower right.

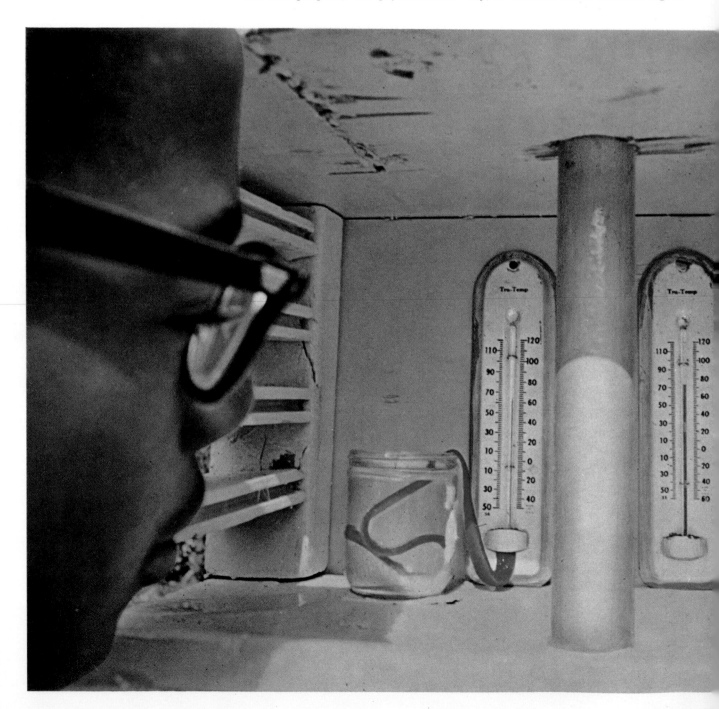

MEASURING MOISTURE

John Sims checks his psychrometer, or wet- and dry-bulb thermometer system *(center)*, and hair hygrometer *(right)*. The hair in the hygrometer lengthens when air is moist and shrinks when it is dry. The psychrometer provides finer measurement of the moisture content of air.

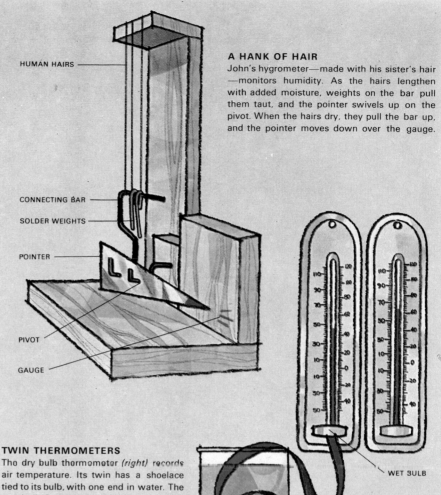

HUMAN HAIRS

CONNECTING BAR

SOLDER WEIGHTS

POINTER

PIVOT

GAUGE

A HANK OF HAIR

John's hygrometer—made with his sister's hair —monitors humidity. As the hairs lengthen with added moisture, weights on the bar pull them taut, and the pointer swivels up on the pivot. When the hairs dry, they pull the bar up, and the pointer moves down over the gauge.

WET BULB

TWIN THERMOMETERS

The dry bulb thermometer *(right)* records air temperature. Its twin has a shoelace tied to its bulb, with one end in water. The wet-bulb figure is less than the dry-bulb because of evaporation from the shoelace. The relationship between wet and dry temperatures establishes relative humidity.

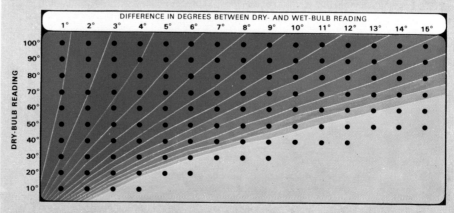

SHOELACE

WATER

FIGURING RELATIVE HUMIDITY

DIFFERENCE IN DEGREES BETWEEN DRY- AND WET-BULB READING

1° 2° 3° 4° 5° 6° 7° 8° 9° 10° 11° 12° 13° 14° 15°

DRY-BULB READING

100° 90° 80° 70° 60° 50° 40° 30° 20° 10°

THE AIR'S MOISTURE CHARTED

In the chart above, the darkest band of color represents a relative humidity of 95 per cent or more. The figure drops off 5 per cent with each lighter band. Subtracting a wet-bulb reading of, say, 65° from a dry-bulb figure of 70° *(left-hand column)* gives a 5° difference *(top line)*. The dot below 5° and opposite 70° is in the 75 per cent relative humidity color band.

A SAILOR'S GUIDE FOR LANDSMEN

WIND SPEED IN MPH	BEAUFORT NUMBER AND WIND EFFECTS ON LAND	OFFICIAL DESIGNATION
LESS THAN 1	0　CALM; SMOKE RISES VERTICALLY	
1-3	1　DIRECTION OF WIND SHOWN BY SMOKE BUT NOT BY WIND VANES	LIGHT
4-7	2　WIND FELT ON FACE; LEAVES RUSTLE; WIND VANES MOVE	
8-12	3　LEAVES AND SMALL TWIGS IN MOTION; WIND EXTENDS LIGHT FLAG	GENTLE
13-18	4　WIND RAISES DUST AND LOOSE PAPER; SMALL BRANCHES MOVE	MODERATE
19-24	5　SMALL TREES IN LEAF BEGIN TO SWAY; CRESTED WAVELETS APPEAR ON INLAND WATERS	FRESH
25-31	6　LARGE BRANCHES MOVE; TELEGRAPH WIRES WHISTLE; UMBRELLAS BECOME UNWIELDY	STRONG
32-38	7　WHOLE TREES SWAY; WALKING INTO WIND IS DIFFICULT	
39-46	8　TWIGS BREAK OFF TREES; CARS VEER ON ROAD	GALE
47-54	9　SLIGHT STRUCTURAL DAMAGE OCCURS (CHIMNEY POTS, ROOF SLATES BLOWN AWAY)	
55-63	10　TREES ARE UPROOTED; CONSIDERABLE STRUCTURAL DAMAGE IS DONE	WHOLE GALE
64-72	11　WIDESPREAD DAMAGE	
73 OR MORE	12　WIDESPREAD DAMAGE	HURRICANE

Reading the Record of the Wind

Wind is weather on the move. If the amateur meteorologist knows the direction of the wind and how fast it is blowing, he can begin to translate the facts into forecast.

The earliest weather forecasters were sailors and farmers, who invented the wind vane to show the wind's direction. In 1806, Admiral Sir Francis Beaufort of the British Navy devised a velocity scale based on the wind's visible effects (lower left). A more recent wind-measuring device is the anemometer, the whirligig that is shown in the picture at left. Mechanically, an anemometer is simple (below), but making it a readable wind speedometer is difficult. After John Sims built his anemometer, he had to convert its revolutions per minute into miles per hour of wind velocity. He rigged a ratchet that clicked at each revolution, and calibrated the anemometer by holding it out a car window and counting the clicks per minute at various speeds.

WHIRLIGIG AND WEATHERCOCK
Tightening a nut on an axle, John overhauls his anemometer. He made it from kitchen funnels and scrap parts, including an old roller-skate wheel. The wind, striking the conical cups, whirls them even in a very light breeze. Behind the anemometer is John's wind vane, or weathercock.

THE ADMIRAL'S TABLE
The Beaufort scale was originally a guide for sailing-ship captains, based on the effect of various wind speeds on sailing ships. It has been modified for landsmen, and this table gives examples of what wind does at different speeds to trees, pedestrians, chimneys and umbrellas.

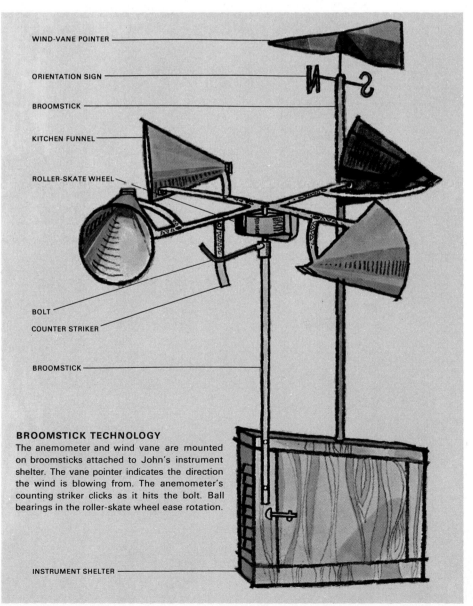

WIND-VANE POINTER

ORIENTATION SIGN

BROOMSTICK

KITCHEN FUNNEL

ROLLER-SKATE WHEEL

BOLT

COUNTER STRIKER

BROOMSTICK

BROOMSTICK TECHNOLOGY
The anemometer and wind vane are mounted on broomsticks attached to John's instrument shelter. The vane pointer indicates the direction the wind is blowing from. The anemometer's counting striker clicks as it hits the bolt. Ball bearings in the roller-skate wheel ease rotation.

INSTRUMENT SHELTER

Pressure Readings in Mineral Oil

In predicting weather John Sims must remember that he lives at the bottom of an ocean of air, and that the pressure of that air frequently changes. How it changes can vitally affect his forecasts. For example, a high-pressure system accompanied by cool, dry air may suddenly give way to low pressure and warm, moist air—causing a switch from fair weather to rain.

To record the ups and downs of air pressure, John built his own barometer, which registers the effect of varying pressures on a column of liquid. John's barometer is filled with mineral oil instead of the mercury used by professionals, but it serves his purpose. When its readings are related to measurements of wind direction (below), John has his first real clues about the approaching weather.

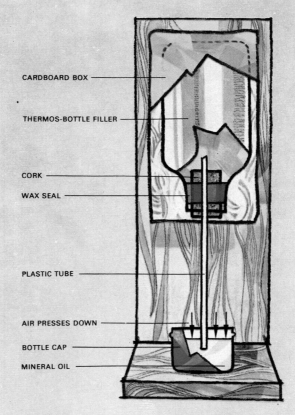

CARDBOARD BOX

THERMOS-BOTTLE FILLER

CORK

WAX SEAL

PLASTIC TUBE

AIR PRESSES DOWN

BOTTLE CAP

MINERAL OIL

REFILLING THE RESERVOIR
John carefully pours mineral oil into his barometer's reservoir. He does not have to keep the instrument outdoors because the atmospheric pressure indoors is almost exactly the same as that outside. But a barometer should be kept where temperature variations will not be severe.

A BASIC BAROMETER
In this homemade barometer, the weight of air pressing down on mineral oil in the bottle cap drives the oil up the plastic tube. The mark on the tube is a reference point for observing pressure changes. The vacuum bottle filler is insulated with rock wool to keep the air in the tube at a constant temperature.

RULES OF THUMB FOR FORECASTERS

WIND DIRECTION	BAROMETER AT SEA LEVEL	KIND OF WEATHER TO BE EXPECTED
SW TO NW	30.10 to 30.20 steady	FAIR WITH LITTLE TEMPERATURE CHANGE FOR ONE OR TWO DAYS
SW TO NW	30.10 to 30.20, rising fast	FAIR, FOLLOWED BY RAIN WITHIN TWO DAYS
SW TO NW	30.20 or above steady	CONTINUED FAIR, WITH LITTLE TEMPERATURE CHANGE
SW TO NW	30.20 or above, falling slowly	SLOWLY RISING TEMPERATURE; FAIR FOR TWO DAYS
S TO SE	30.10 to 30.20, falling slowly	RAIN WITHIN 24 HOURS
S TO SE	30.10 to 30.20, falling fast	WIND RISING IN FORCE; RAIN IN 12 TO 24 HOURS
SE TO NE	30.10 to 30.20, falling slowly	RAIN IN 12 TO 18 HOURS
SE TO NE	30.10 to 30.20, falling fast	RISING WIND; RAIN WITHIN 12 HOURS
E TO NE	30.10 or above, falling slowly	IN SUMMER, LIGHT WINDS, RAIN NOT IMMEDIATELY LIKELY; IN WINTER, RAIN IN 24 HOURS
E TO NE	30.10 or above, falling fast	RAIN PROBABLE IN SUMMER WITHIN 24 HOURS; IN WINTER, RAIN OR SNOW AND WINDY
SE TO NE	30.00 or below, falling slowly	STEADY RAIN FOR ONE OR TWO DAYS
SE TO NE	30.00 or below, falling fast	RAIN AND HIGH WIND, CLEARING WITHIN 36 HOURS
S TO SW	30.00 or below, rising slowly	CLEARING WITHIN A FEW HOURS, FAIR FOR SEVERAL DAYS
S TO E	29.80 or below, falling fast	SEVERE STORM IMMINENT; CLEARING WITHIN 24 HOURS; COLDER IN WINTER
E TO N	29.80 or below, falling fast	SEVERE NORTHEAST GALE, HEAVY RAIN; IN WINTER, HEAVY SNOW AND COLD WAVE
GOING TO W	29.80 or below, rising fast	CLEARING AND COLDER

WIND AND PRESSURE GUIDELINES
This chart summarizes decades of meteorological experience in the Northeast region, where John lives. In this section, winds from the west almost always bring high-pressure readings and good weather, while those from an easterly direction generally mean a falling barometer and rain or snow. A wind that swings from easterly to westerly usually brings with it a swift and welcome change—from bad weather to good.

167

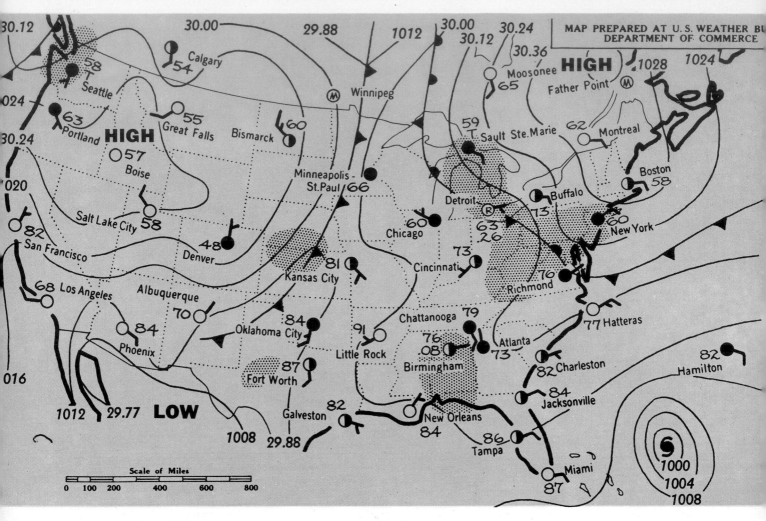

U.S. WEATHER IN SHORTHAND

The most prominent features of a weather map are the whorls signifying lines of equal pressure —called isobars—and the toothlike symbols denoting frontal systems. In this map isobars are marked at one end with barometric pressure in inches and at the other end in millibars, smaller units of pressure that equal approximately 3/100 of an inch; high- and low-pressure systems are indicated. Shaded areas mark precipitation, and the circles and tails show local cloud cover and wind data. Single numbers near the circles are temperature readings; a second number underneath gives inches of precipitation, if any. Other symbols are explained below. The map on the opposite page shows the same weather pictorially: clear areas are indicated by a bright sun, fronts by lines of clouds, and so on. This map has one highly unusual feature: a hurricane just off the Florida coast. Major weather systems usually show an eastward movement of 500 to 700 miles per day.

HOW TO READ THE WEATHER MAP

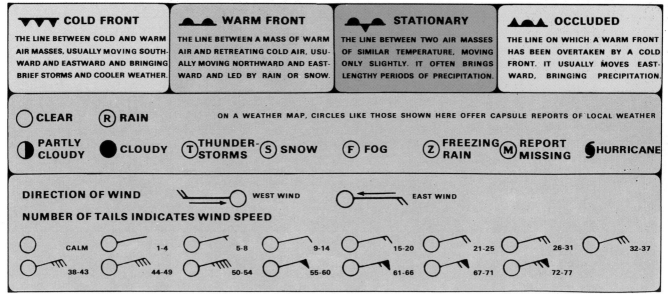

COLD FRONT
THE LINE BETWEEN COLD AND WARM AIR MASSES, USUALLY MOVING SOUTHWARD AND EASTWARD AND BRINGING BRIEF STORMS AND COOLER WEATHER.

WARM FRONT
THE LINE BETWEEN A MASS OF WARM AIR AND RETREATING COLD AIR, USUALLY MOVING NORTHWARD AND EASTWARD AND LED BY RAIN OR SNOW.

STATIONARY
THE LINE BETWEEN TWO AIR MASSES OF SIMILAR TEMPERATURE, MOVING ONLY SLIGHTLY. IT OFTEN BRINGS LENGTHY PERIODS OF PRECIPITATION.

OCCLUDED
THE LINE ON WHICH A WARM FRONT HAS BEEN OVERTAKEN BY A COLD FRONT. IT USUALLY MOVES EASTWARD, BRINGING PRECIPITATION.

CLEAR   RAIN   ON A WEATHER MAP, CIRCLES LIKE THOSE SHOWN HERE OFFER CAPSULE REPORTS OF LOCAL WEATHER

PARTLY CLOUDY   CLOUDY   THUNDERSTORMS   SNOW   FOG   FREEZING RAIN   REPORT MISSING   HURRICANE

DIRECTION OF WIND   WEST WIND   EAST WIND

NUMBER OF TAILS INDICATES WIND SPEED

CALM   1-4   5-8   9-14   15-20   21-25   26-31   32-37

38-43   44-49   50-54   55-60   61-66   67-71   72-77

Projecting the Big Picture

The fact that John's home "weather bureau" boasts only one station puts him in the position of a ship captain without a chart; all he knows is what is visible from his own bridge. John's instruments—which include a gauge for measuring rainfall and a nephoscope, a device which observes the movement of fronts by tracking the drift of high clouds—do a good job of giving him a local weather picture. But local weather is a product of diverse weather situations taking place over a vast area. In order to make a local forecast accurate, the meteorologist must have a general picture of the weather over the entire nation.

Such a picture (*opposite, above*) appears every day in John's local newspaper. Adapted from the U.S. Weather Bureau maps, it plots the daily weather situation across the whole country, using special meteorological symbols (*opposite, below*) to describe local conditions. (For comparison, the same conditions are shown pictorially on the map above.)

By itself, one day's weather map is no more useful to the forecaster, amateur or professional, than only one reading per day of his instruments would be. To keep track of the trend of local weather, he must read all his instruments several times daily. To establish a general pattern for the weather, several days' maps must be studied in succession. Then, equipped with the latest maps, the records taken from his instruments and his own deductive powers, the weatherman is ready to get down to the brass tacks of his calling—making a prediction.

HELP FROM AN OLD HAND
At the Weather Bureau, John goes over the day's map with forecaster Mel Oppenheimer. Oppenheimer is demonstrating how the map is assembled from a mass of nationwide reports.

169

The Reward: A Look into the Future

Forecasting weather is a little like gambling, but with one big difference. Weathermen do not make predictions just for the pleasure of winning. In fact, they get little credit when they are right, and they are often criticized when the weather lets them down.

Yet meteorologists, like gamblers, live by making educated guesses. The more educated the guess, the greater its accuracy. Between John Sims, with his simple instruments, and the U.S. Weather Bureau, with its multi-million-dollar facilities, there is only a difference of degree. In one series of forecasts which John made, his average was a little better than .500. The Weather Bureau average is .850. But the reward John gets from his hobby is richer than any average would indicate. When he looks at a brilliant sky at evening he sees more than a pretty sunset; in its pattern of clouds, in the vivid colors of the sky itself, he can see partway into the future.

MAKING THE FORECAST
In his bedroom, amid charts showing types of clouds *(rear)* and some of the rules of forecasting *(left),* John works on preparation of a forecast. In front of him on the desk, next to his homemade barometer, stand a new hygrometer and an aneroid barometer, both gifts.

STUDYING THE SKY
A simple forecasting formula for John, as he studies a sunset, is the old saying, "Sky red at night, sailor's delight"—meaning fair skies tomorrow. If skies to the west are clear, the air holds more dust than moisture. The sun's rays break up on the dust, taking on a red tinge.

8
An Awesome Future

DESPITE ALL THAT MAN HAS LEARNED about heat, wind and rain in the last 100 years, science today is on the threshold of an even better understanding of the atmosphere and its behavior.

This broader comprehension will bring many benefits—better forecasts, better conservation of water resources, more abundant food, cleaner skies. It will make air and sea travel safer. It will help guide spacebound voyagers past the vast upper-air winds, through the perilous radiation belts, the bands of meteoric dust and safely home again. It may even place in man's hand the awesome power to change the weather—to make it rain, prevent a hurricane, add more heat to earth, temper hailstorms—to exert a profound influence, in short, over natural forces that have shaped the destinies of all living things for millions of years.

Man's chance of realizing these dreams lies to a great extent in his command of amazing new tools—ever more delicate and cunning electronic sensors, complex and faster computers, more sophisticated and far-ranging satellites.

One of the astonishing new instruments at man's disposal is the laser (the name is derived from the words Light Amplification by Stimulated Emission of Radiation). The laser, not much bigger than a flashlight, shoots out a concentrated ray of light in thin, pencil-like beams, or pulses, that can reach to the moon, burn holes in steel plate, drill a diamond. In weather research, laser reflections bouncing off distant objects can be used for scanning and identification in the same way that radar uses reflected radio waves. For this reason, some call the new device "laser radar."

The full capabilities of laser radar have not been tested, but there are signs that its reflected beams not only indicate the presence of such objects as microscopic particles and water droplets, but are even affected by clear-air turbulence. Laser radar may make it possible to determine whether cloud particles are ice or water; to measure the speed of approaching clouds and fog at distances far beyond the range of present instruments; to study microscopic particles in the upper atmosphere, and to detect clear-air turbulence in the paths of high-flying jet aircraft.

Another fascinating research tool now coming into use is the working model of an actual atmospheric process, for close-hand study in the laboratory. One such miniature is an ingenious model of the circulation of air over a hemisphere, perfected by researchers at the University of Chicago. A round, flat-bottomed pan, representing a flattened-out hemisphere, is fitted with a cooler at the center, or pole, and heaters along the rim, or equator. The pan is filled with an inch of water, representing the atmosphere; when dye is dropped into this mixture of hot and cold water, it reveals patterns of flow. Then the pan is rotated to simulate the earth's rotation. Tiny cyclones and anticyclones form in the middle

AN AUTOMATIC WEATHER EYE
A bobbing, anchored weather station named NOMAD (Navy Oceanographic Meteorological Automatic Device) maintains a storm-detection service far out at sea. Equipped with high-powered telemetry systems, NOMADs detect, report and survive ocean gales and full-blown hurricanes. Small windmills generate power for this NOMAD; others have nuclear generators.

latitudes. Eddies appear in the same zone and form the sinuous wreath of the westerlies. An easterly current forms near the equator. Meteorologists are careful not to draw too close a parallel between a global hemisphere and a small dishpan of water—the friction effects of the atmosphere as it works against the earth cannot be exactly duplicated, for example—but the currents revealed by the dye bear an astonishing resemblance to a typical hemispheric weather map.

Tornado in a test tube

An equally ingenious miniature is the test-tube tornado created by dropping salt crystals or other nuclei into a rotating beaker of ordinary club soda. The carbon dioxide in the soda forms bubbles around the nuclei, fizzing like an opened bottle of pop. The bubbles rise, and owing to the spin of the liquid, move toward the center of rotation. There, an intense funnel-shaped vortex materializes. In effect, a tiny tornado whirls within the beaker, where scientists can observe it at their leisure.

A model of the atmosphere can even be created entirely out of numbers. Just as mathematicians can translate the flight of a rocket or the engineering of a suspension bridge into numerical values that can be fed into an electronic computer, so it is theoretically possible to construct a numerical model of weather as it exists around the earth at any given moment. For more than a decade ESSA's Geophysical Fluid Dynamics Laboratory, in Washington, D.C., has been working toward this end, conducting experiments on the most advanced computers available. The programs are so complex that the simulation of one day of weather requires almost 24 hours of computer time on a machine capable of executing one million instructions per second. For such techniques to be useful in analyzing and forecasting weather on a regular, day-to-day basis, meteorologists will need computers that operate 50 to 100 times faster than present models.

In a typical experiment today, 400,000 bits of numerical data are fed into a computer programmed with 15,000 separate instructions for processing details of the weather at 100,000 points at earth level and nine higher levels reaching to the tropopause. Applying the instructions, the computer is put to work to predict what the temperature, wind speed, wind direction and humidity will be at each of those 100,000 points five minutes later. The machine then proceeds to compute the next five-minute forecast. A simulated 150-day flow, the customary duration of a test run, requires more than one and a half trillion computer operations.

Compared to the real atmosphere, these computer models of the weather are as yet quite crude. However, they already provide weathermen with reasonably accurate forecasts up to a week in advance of storms evolving in the temperate zones. For much longer periods than that the models have shown a remarkable ability to reproduce many of the semi-permanent features of the real atmosphere, such as the jet streams. The main difficulties impeding further progress are three: an inability to model the effects of cumulus clouds; a poor understanding of the way energy is dissipated in the atmosphere; and insufficient data to detail fully the structure of the atmosphere.

The goal of such models is an accuracy and refinement that will enable meteorologists to program into a computer the state of the atmosphere at any given moment and have the machine print out a near-flawless prediction of what the weather will be a day or a week later. Once models attain this degree of verisimilitude, they can be used not only for prediction but also to experiment with weather. Scientists will disturb the model—"jimmy the inputs," as one scientist phrases it—to learn what might happen if they disturbed the natural atmosphere in the same way. Thus, numerical models, when they have attained the requisite fidelity to the real atmosphere, will make it possible for scientists to tell what the far-reaching effects on California weather might be if, for example, the Mojave Desert were watered and turned into a green valley.

Phenomena of the "ignorosphere"

In a different but equally vital area of research, meteorologists are relying heavily on another modern technological triumph—the upper-atmosphere sounding rocket. Between 20 and 120 miles out from the surface of the earth, there exists a strange region of ozone layers, X-rays, ultraviolet rays, meteoric dust, weirdly illuminated clouds and bitter cold. This region includes the upper stratosphere, the mesosphere and the lower ionosphere. Scientists know so little about this part of the atmosphere that some of them wryly refer to it as the "ignorosphere."

The first organized instrumental exploration of the upper atmosphere took place during the International Geophysical Year, 1957-1958. The IGY studies, conducted at the height of the sun's 11-year cycle of sunspot activity, confirmed what meterologists had long suspected: that solar weather exercises an appreciable influence on earth weather. To supplement the IGY findings, during the period 1964-1965, with solar activity at an expected low, scientists of several nations launched a program to fire thousands of sounding rockets into the upper atmosphere to amass astronomical, geophysical and meteorological data. This period of joint effort was dubbed the International Years of the Quiet Sun.

Hard, practical considerations lend unusual urgency to such studies of solar and space weather. As an example, for a long time to come, the U.S. aerospace program and air industry will need more information about atmospheric conditions that will be encountered by space flights and by high-altitude aircraft. What are the wind speeds in the mesosphere?

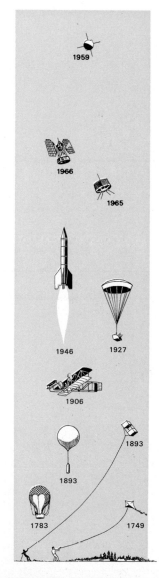

THE EVOLUTION OF DEVICES for studying the atmosphere, from kites to space platforms, spanned some two centuries. After kites, meteorologists sent up instruments in manned balloons, then in free balloons, aircraft and rockets. Among the latest devices are the satellites shown, from top: Vanguard II, Nimbus II and the television-equipped Tiros X.

175

What air densities will be encountered on re-entry into the mesosphere, the stratosphere, the troposphere? Is there any potentially damaging radiation? Are there dangerous, man-made radiation belts from nuclear testing? The U.S. aerospace program cannot wait 10 or 20 years for answers. It must have them quickly or design around the problem, at heavy costs in money and manpower.

Moreover, the more man knows about solar and space weather, the sooner he will reach an understanding of weather on earth. A solar flare suddenly shoots a stupendous tongue of cosmic flame 50,000 miles above the surface of the sun, then, just as suddenly, subsides. Almost instantly here on earth, all shortwave radio communication is blacked out over whichever hemisphere is lighted by the sun. Streams of high-energy particles hit the earth's atmosphere. Other ionized particles arrive a day or so later, producing magnetic storms and shimmering displays of aurora.

Do these awesome solar storms affect the changing weather of earth —and if so, how? In search of answers, rockets equipped with Geiger counters, ionization chambers, particle samplers and other detection devices blast off launching pads in the Bahamas, Manitoba, the South Atlantic, the Antarctic and northern Sweden.

Reports from space

The newest, most spectacular tool of all—the one which most presages the automated electronic weather-surveillance system of the future—is the weather satellite. These stations in outer space serve two functions: to record and send back to earth data on space weather, and to take pictures of the earth and its cloud cover from a great distance.

The world's first all-weather satellite, named Tiros (Television Infrared Observation Satellite), was launched in 1960, and was followed in the next few years by a number of sister satellites. The first Tiros went into orbit about 450 miles in space—a little above the floor of the exosphere—and circled the earth once every hour and 39 minutes. Its instruments measured such things as the absorption and reflection of solar energy by the atmosphere, but of most immediate interest to meteorologists were its two midget television cameras, each about the size of a water glass, for taking pictures of earth. One had a wide-angle lens that photographed an area 750 miles square, the other a narrow-angle lens that photographed an area 75 miles square.

Successive Tiros satellites transmitted pictures of vast, hemispheric sweeps of cloud patterns that were brewing and fomenting tomorrow's weather. The pictures were taken not only above populated regions, but also above hitherto inaccessible expanses—deserts, polar ice fields, remote reaches of the South Atlantic and Pacific Oceans and the steamy latitudes of the tropics. A number of hurricanes were detected.

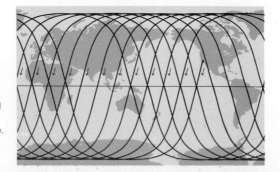

A SPIRAL OF ORBITS traces the route of Nimbus, the first satellite designed to monitor the weather over every portion of the globe each 24 hours. Launched from Point Mugu, California, in August 1964, Nimbus orbited near the poles and shifted its track westward 28° at the equator with every orbit. As it circled the globe once every 98.3 minutes, one of its camera systems transmitted continuous pictures of cloud conditions to receiving stations on the ground under its route.

Tiros satellites were, indeed, in the words of one scientist, almost "too darned successful." They sent pictures and data earthward like unthinking robots, in an unceasing stream that overwhelmed existing facilities for analyzing and processing them. Researchers had to skim off the best and file the rest for later study.

Despite the flood of pictures they transmitted, the Tiros satellites were primitive by later standards. The automatic Tiros cameras spent much of their time in orbit shooting pictures of empty space. When they were aimed at earth they often shot grotesquely distorted pictures from oblique angles. "Fitting them together," remarked Dr. Verner E. Suomi, the Weather Bureau's chief scientist, "was like tearing a bunch of unnumbered pages out of a novel, scattering them at random all over the room, and then trying to put them back in order."

In August 1964, when Nimbus, a $100 million satellite developed by NASA's Goddard Space Flight Center, was rocketed into a near-polar orbit, its improvement over Tiros was instantly evident. Equipped with cells to convert solar energy into electrical energy for its batteries, Nimbus was the first weather satellite with cameras continuously oriented toward earth. It sent down more than 1,000 pictures a day. Some sequences showed strips of the earth's surface almost from one pole to the other. Nimbus' most gratifying advance, however, was the quality of its nighttime, infrared photographs. Far exceeding expectations, they were almost as clear as Tiros' daylight pictures, and made possible for the first time an around-the-clock surveillance of the earth's cloud patterns.

Even as Nimbus went aloft, scientists were at work on even better satellites. Meteorologists anticipate the day when massive nuclear-powered weather satellites will be precisely placed in space. Even sooner they hope to have satellites synchronized for the continuous scanning of the entire globe between 60° latitude north and south.

The life record of a storm

Photographs from these future craft will enable experts to trace every major storm from birth to demise. Radar and laser radar on board will read the vertical depth of cloud layers, and the intensity and distribution of precipitation. Other sensors will measure infrared radiation from the earth and the atmosphere. The satellites may even be equipped with small digital computers for preliminary data-processing. A possible alternative is a manned satellite, fitted with computer systems and functioning as an orbiting data-processing center for world-wide distribution of weather information.

As envisaged today, the satellites of the future will supplement a gradually extended system of ground- and low-level devices. These will probably include fixed, unmanned land stations capable of transmitting

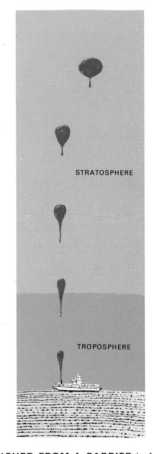

STRATOSPHERE

TROPOSPHERE

LAUNCHED FROM A CARRIER in 1960, the huge balloon shown above was part of Operation Skyhook 60, an upper-atmosphere research project sponsored jointly by the U.S. Navy, the University of Chicago and the National Science Foundation. Designed to explore weather conditions above 110,000 feet, the balloons remained aloft for up to 33½ hours. From instruments and from ground observation of the balloons, meteorologists learned for the first time that the near-vacuum of the stratosphere has a daily changing pattern of winds that blow at up to 150 mph.

dependable reports from remote polar, desert and wilderness areas; both anchored and free-floating automatic marine stations for collecting data from now uncovered ocean expanses and, finally, constant-level balloons that will float around the earth in the upper troposphere and stratosphere, sending back data on temperature and winds. Some 2,000 of these plastic balloons may drift with the globe-girdling winds, carrying cheap but efficient miniature electronics systems printed on plastic.

Controlling the weather

With these new and strange-sounding tools, man is striving with all his intelligence and ingenuity to learn everything there is to know about the atmosphere. If he succeeds, his prize will be a vastly improved ability to predict the weather reliably. Then, once he can make predictions with certainty, he may dare start on the second great adventure with weather: attempts to control it on a large scale to suit his own ends.

Man has already altered his weather drastically—without meaning to, and much of the time to his own disadvantage. His vast cities are the leading offenders. They change wind flow, warm the atmosphere and cast pollutants into the sky. Weather Bureau scientists estimate that the typical large industrial city today receives up to 25 per cent less wind than its surrounding countryside because of its high buildings and convection currents. These currents, plus condensation nuclei, cause up to 10 per cent more rainfall and double the number of winter fogs. Its mean winter temperature is warmer than that of nearby rural areas by 2° or 3°F. The pall of acrid, throat-searing, eye-burning smog over big industrial centers like London and Los Angeles is so thick that even the sun's more penetrating emissions—light and ultraviolet waves—have difficulty getting through it. London and Manchester have about 30 minutes less daylight, 45 minutes less sunshine and 50 per cent less ultraviolet radiation per day than their rural environs.

Man's chimneys and combustion engines are sending about 12 billion tons of carbon dioxide a year into the earth's atmosphere. In the next 50 years, this rate may quadruple. Such an increase, by trapping more heat, may raise the earth's average temperature by 1° or 2°F.—and that, in turn, might over an extended period of time melt the Greenland ice cap and the vast Antarctic ice fields, raise the level of the oceans by 170 feet, swamp every port and seacoast in the world and push the shores of the Gulf of Mexico north to Memphis, Tennessee.

Not all the changes wrought by man need be undesirable, of course. There are many more beneficial changes he would like to bring about if he could, and a number of grandiose schemes have been proposed to achieve some of these ends. Here are a few of them:
• Blacken the Arctic ice with carbon. This would reduce the loss of solar

energy by reflection, and make northern wastelands more habitable.
• Reduce evaporation over large areas of ocean by coating them with a chemical such as hexadecanol, which acts as a water sealer to reduce evaporation. The effect would be to reduce rain in some regions, while moderating tropical storms.
• Create a five-mile-thick ice cloud over the Arctic by exploding 10 "clean" hydrogen bombs of 10 megatons each beneath the surface of the Arctic Ocean. The steam cloud from the explosion would fountain high into the atmosphere, condense into water droplets and freeze. The resulting ice-crystal cloud would prevent the escape of infrared radiation back into space, add heat to the atmospheric engine and might change the dynamics of the general circulation to improve the world's climate.
• Dam the 55-mile-wide Bering Strait and use nuclear power to pump icy Arctic Ocean water through the dam into the Pacific Ocean. Warm water from the Atlantic would replace the cold water, thus improving the year-round weather of the Arctic.

There have also been proposals for modifying weather on a smaller scale. One of them would make the barren Nevada desert bloom by blasting gaps through the Sierra Nevada to permit the passage of moist Pacific air. Another would attempt to get rid of Los Angeles smog by submerging a 100- by 200-mile polyethylene shield in 100 feet of water off the Southern California coast. According to the theory, evaporation of the warmed water over the shield would generate convective thunderstorms. These, in turn, would sweep pollution from Los Angeles.

These projects present technological and economic problems of a Himalayan order. For instance, the laying-down of a .004-inch layer of carbon black over the area extending from the North Pole to 65°N. lat. would require 1.5 billion tons of carbon dust. If it were distributed from C-124 Globemaster transports capable of carrying 10 tons, the planes would have to fly some 150 million sorties to accomplish the job. "This," one scientist has commented dryly, "would take considerable time."

The dangers of tampering

But suppose the logistics of such a project were solved and the feat were done? Would the results be a blessing or a curse? No one can be sure. The idea of damming the Bering Strait was advanced by a Russian engineer in 1959. The next year, another Russian scientist pointed out that it would probably be disastrous. Among the immediate effects of even a slight warming of the Arctic, he said, would be a decrease in precipitation in Soviet Russia that would ruin the nation's economy. Other scientists have suggested that ultimately there would be a large and dangerous increase in the water-vapor content of Arctic air, with the result that all the continents of the Northern Hemisphere would be vis-

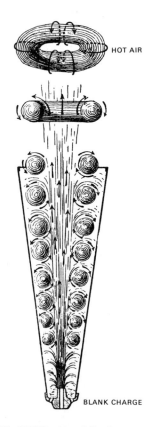

HOT AIR

BLANK CHARGE

ANTI-HAIL GUNS, shaped like huge megaphones, were exhibited around 1900 in northern Italy, where hail is a frequent crop destroyer. Shown at left in the main square of Padua, the cannon fired a blank charge *(above),* which blew a doughnut of hot air up into the clouds. Although the doughnuts rarely reached the altitude of hail-bearing clouds, it was believed their impact dispersed hail formations. Before they were debunked by systematic tests, there were about 2,500 of these guns in use.

ited by more and bigger winter storms. Heavy, frequent snows would smite coastal areas. Existing glaciers would grow and new ones would form. Temperate regions would be threatened by a new ice age.

The disagreement between the two Soviet scientists points up the chief flaw in visionary plans for weather modification. There is no simple way of knowing all the consequences of a major meteorological innovation. A technique for breaking a Great Plains drought might produce a citrus-killing freeze in Florida. A way to temper winter in North America and Northern Europe might turn marginal rainfall areas—Southern California, the French Riviera—into deserts.

But with incalculable benefits at stake for society and mankind, scientists hope to find out what can be done safely to improve the world's weather. To aid in this effort they count on the development of new instruments, new theories, new experiments, computers from 100 to 1,000 times faster than those available today. "It is entirely possible," Dr. Vannevar Bush told the Government's Advisory Committee on Weather Control in 1957, "that were he wise enough, man could produce favorable effects, perhaps of enormous practical significance, transforming his environment to render it more salutary for his purposes. This is certainly a matter which should be studied assiduously and explored vigorously. . . . By all means let us get at it."

The New Science of Weather

When they consider the future of their art, meteorologists are cautious forecasters. They know that the accuracy of their weather predictions for the U.S. in 1942 was probably less than 80 per cent and has not improved more than 5 per cent since then. But there is one significant difference now: forecasts today look further into the future and thus run a greater risk of being wrong. Furthermore, the talk and the writing of some research meteorologists have begun to carry a new optimism—a hint that breakthroughs may be in the offing. New lines of research made possible by recent tools hold the promise of dramatic advances in weather prediction. The most important of these tools have been weather satellites and computers (opposite), but other developments—such as new kinds of lasers, radar and automatic weather stations—are also contributing toward making meteorology one of the most exciting "new" sciences around.

SCRIBBLING TOMORROW'S WEATHER

The machine in the foreground is a Weather Bureau "data plotter," which makes upper-air pressure and wind predictions for the Northern Hemisphere 24 hours in advance, based on current readings that have been processed by a computer. For this photograph, a small light was attached to the plotting arm to trace the lines drawn on the map. The map takes about three minutes to draw.

MAJOR SHIPPING ROUTES

ASIA

EUROPE

AFRICA

NORTH AMERICA

SOUTH AMERICA

A Far-flung
but Patchy Network

The standard approach to weather prediction relies upon sheer volume of weather data. Scattered about the globe over 2,000 observation posts, in a unique example of international cooperation, relay their data to central locations where experts try to assemble a composite picture of Northern Hemisphere weather. Similar attempts are only beginning for the Southern Hemisphere. But even in areas where weather stations are most dense—Western Europe and the United States—they are still too few to give more than a blurred outline of the situation. And in those re-

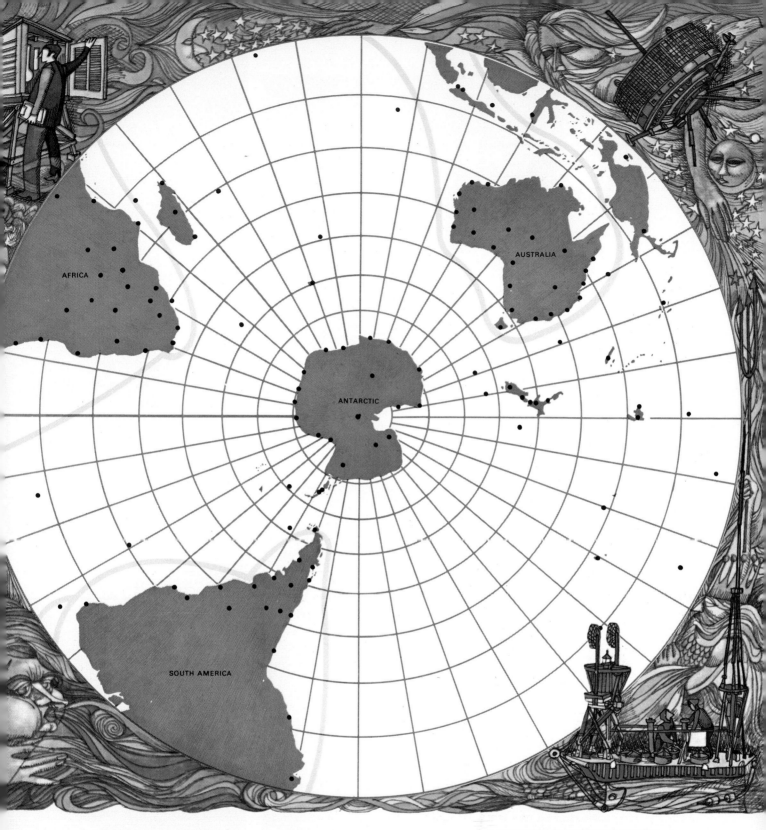

Map labels: AFRICA, AUSTRALIA, ANTARCTIC, SOUTH AMERICA

gions where most weather begins—the polar and equatorial regions—there are almost no stations at all.

Experts see two solutions to the problem: devices like those around the edges of the map above, and new theories that will make possible a better job with existing stations.

A PROBLEM AND ITS SOLUTIONS

The major weather stations shown on this map suggest the uneven global distribution of data-gathering facilities. Data also come from shipping routes. Some of the devices now in use or planned to fill the gaps are shown in the borders *(clockwise from lower left)*. They are: long-lived radio-equipped balloons drifting around the globe; the Nimbus experimental satellite; manned and unmanned weather outposts; Tiros operational satellites; weather buoys; and radar to extend the range of present stations.

INSTANT WEATHER PICTURES

This bedspringlike antenna is part of the Automatic Picture Transmission (APT) receiver that catches weather pictures from American satellites. The receivers have been installed in a number of nations, and even commercial news media can buy the $32,000 receiving equipment.

The View from the Top

Until recently, weather observers were in the discouraging position of never being able to see the storm around them for all the clouds and rain. Rarely was anyone able to find much pattern in the masses of clouds that rolled overhead. But the coming of the cloud-photographing satellites —first Tiros, then Nimbus—has given new importance to cloud-watching.

For example, one of the early discoveries made by these satellites was that clouds almost always come in large, organized "cloud societies"; that is, each cloud is part of a distinctive pattern, such as a hurricane or frontal line. Hopefully, each pattern will turn out to have a predictable behavior. Meteorologists are now tackling the identification of all the different cloud societies and the cataloguing of their behavior.

One of the experts, Dr. Myron Ligda, sums up the usefulness of satellites: "Every day, people make their plans by glancing at the clouds in the sky. The view is much better from an altitude of several hundred miles."

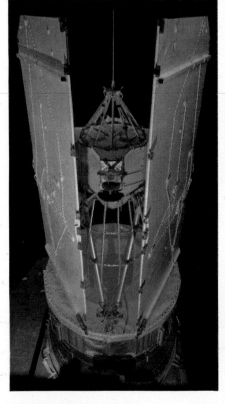

STRETCHING ITS WINGS

An experimental Nimbus satellite undergoes tests *(above)* with its solar-cell "wings" folded for launching. The 5,250 cells on each wing manufacture electricity from solar radiation to power the satellite. At right, a time exposure shows how the wings begin unfolding in orbit.

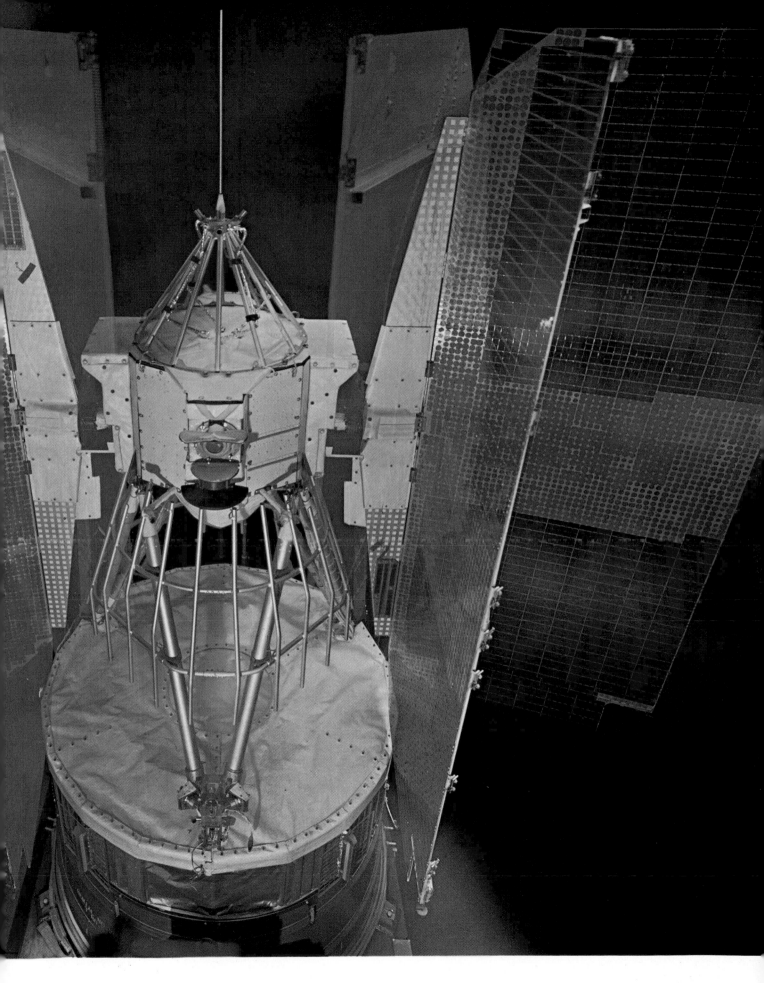

New Steps toward Robot Forecasting

As ever-greater quantities of information inundate them, meteorologists are turning more and more to electronic computers. These machines not only are able to absorb and keep track of an enormous flow of facts, but, programmed with the appropriate formulas, they can even make predictions. In this respect, they have actually proved themselves better than experienced human forecasters.

Now programs are under way to "teach" electronic machines to look at satellite photographs, to recognize what they see—and then, from their superhuman memories, to dredge up vital clues to what weather is in store.

A SATELLITE'S NIGHT SIGHT

A U.S. Weather Bureau meteorologist looks over a 70-millimeter image of a hurricane, as transmitted by Nimbus. The picture was taken at night by infrared radiation. Cuba is near the middle of the frame; at left is Yucatán, Mexico; a portion of South America is at the bottom.

SWITCHBOARD TO THE WORLD

Through the communications equipment above, weather data from all over the world can funnel into the National Meteorological Center at Suitland, Maryland, for processing. The Moscow circuit, for example, may be switched to telephone receivers for voice, to Teletype machines for written material, or to photo-facsimile machines for photographs and weather maps.

STORM PORTRAIT IN LETTERS

A computer's interpretation of what a Pacific typhoon looks like is printed out above. Electronic machines scanned an actual weather-satellite photograph, then converted its various shades of gray into the letters and symbols that are printed here. The purpose of such a system is to turn the photograph's features into symbols which a computer can make use of later.

Examining the Anatomy of a Cloud

Because satellite photographs merely show cloud formations, one result of their use has been a vastly increased interest in just what a cloud is and does. Scientists have learned that, far from being a structureless aerial mist, a cloud has intricate inner mechanisms that manufacture much of the world's weather. Inside clouds may be patches of rain arranged in systematic patterns and currents of air that transport heat from one level of the atmosphere to another—and thus keep the weather brewing.

But the new findings have raised new questions. How do you see inside a cloud? How do you find and measure its currents? Scientists believe that if they had the answers, a satellite cloud photograph would tell them more accurately what sort of weather is ahead. To probe inside the cloud's milky masses, they are putting a number of new gadgets to work. Among these are new radars able to measure the movements of rain clouds and to track the moving boundary where a mass of cold air meets a mass of warm air to form a weather front. Piercing-bright laser beams can penetrate many layers of fog, disclosing the composition of each layer and showing what precipitation it contains. Cloud anatomy may prove to be the most fruitful research in the meteorology of the future.

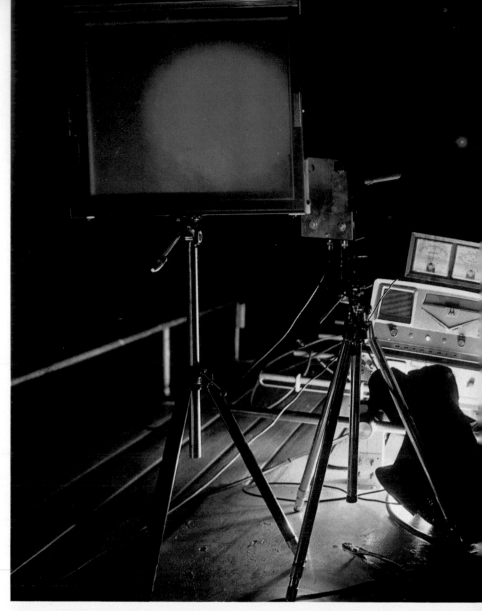

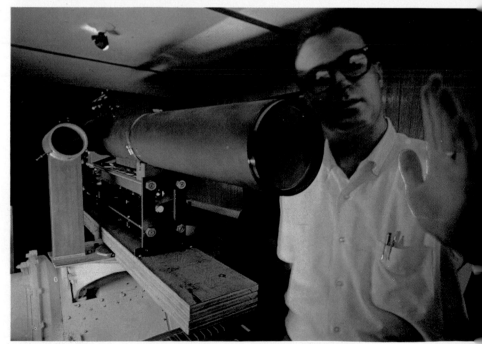

MEASURING THE CLOUDS

An experimental radar installation at the Air Force's Cambridge Research Laboratories in Massachusetts does valuable research into how rain is created. The small antenna at the right focuses a radar beam that measures height, sizes and vertical speeds of snow or rain particles—data that hopefully will lead to new theories about how and when precipitation occurs.

GETTING THE RANGE ON RAIN

Valuable weather research is being done with Doppler radars, which measure speed by noting the change in reflected radar waves, whose frequency changes just as the pitch of a train's whistle changes as it passes by. A Doppler scope measures the movement of rain and snow particles *(left)*. The position, size and movement of the rightmost pulse on the broad green line indicates the particles' height, size and number and their speed up or down. Another scope *(below)* measures the extent of clouds (shown on the horizontal scale) and their velocity (by the height of the white pulses).

CATCHING LASER BEAMS FROM AFAR

Scientists at Boulder, Colorado, test new experimental equipment for making atmospheric measurements. The light beam from a laser 585 yards at rear makes a circular spot on the screen in the foreground. Temperature, pressures and humidity change the beam's outline, which can be measured by equipment in front of the men. Other lasers might measure wind.

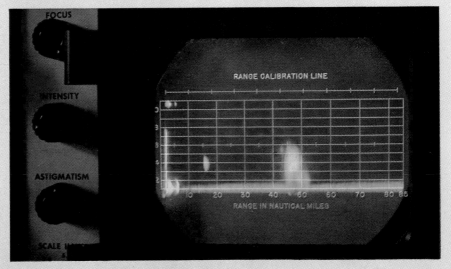

ENLARGING THE LASER

A laser light beam strikes the hand of a National Bureau of Standards scientist at Boulder. To focus the beam over long distances, a telescopic lens system is used and this enlarges the laser beam's diameter from its original two tenths of an inch to the six inches shown here.

The Long Reach of Meteorology

With the coming of exotic tools capable of reaching deep into the heavens, meteorologists are looking to the upper atmosphere and space for the sources of the earth's weather.

From time to time, for example, scientists have noted a possible connection between the weather and sunspots. Long tongues of radiation are known to streak out from sun to earth during sunspot periods; now, with radar observatories such as that at right, the ionizing effects of these particles on the atmosphere 50 miles up can be detected. Attempts are being made to determine whether they play a role in creating weather. Other studies are being made to learn whether meteoric dust from space may provide the nuclei on which water vapor freezes to form ice crystals —and perhaps eventually rain.

As their equipment grows more sophisticated and far-ranging, the ambitions of meteorologists themselves soar higher. They venture one prediction: not only will their record of accuracy improve but the forecasts they will be willing to make will extend further into the chancy future.

UPPER AIR SIGNAL SNARE

This 22-acre array at Lima, Peru, is really one transmitting and receiving antenna. It transmits signals upward, then catches them when they bounce back from the atmosphere above 50 miles. The strength of the return signals permits measurement of upper air ion content.

The Highs and Lows of U.S. Temperature

Although 48 states of the continental U.S. lie in the North Temperate Zone and have a mild average temperature range of 40° to 70°F., they also have highs and lows almost as extreme as any in the world. In winter, each of these states has at one time or another experienced below-zero temperatures; in summer each has sweltered in 100° heat or higher. Indeed, much of the country is hotter in summer than most equatorial regions ever get. On the other hand, in some parts of the northern U.S., there are year-round killing frosts. The maps on this page, prepared by Dr. David Ludlum, show extremes of heat and cold, with dots to indicate where the readings were taken. Figures for Hawaii and Alaska are given in the captions accompanying the maps. Throughout the U.S., the greatest temperature extremes occur in inland regions, far from the oceans and their moderating effect on temperature.

U.S. RECORD TEMPERATURES

EXTREMES OF BITTER COLD . . .

U.S. cold-weather statistics contain a number of surprises. In the mountains of California, the record cold is −45° only three degrees above Maine's low of −48°. Florida has had only one below-zero reading in modern times. Both the extreme and mildest records for cold are in two states not shown: Alaska, with −76° and Hawaii, with a moderate 14°.

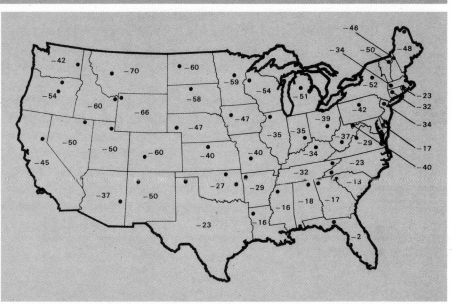

. . . AND BLAZING HEAT

The record high-temperature reading in the U.S., 134°, is held by Death Valley, California. North Dakota, which has one of the coldest records (−60°), also owns one of the hottest (121°). Other extremes are Idaho (−60°, 118°), Montana (−70°, 117°) and Wyoming (−66°, 114°). Alaska and Hawaii have experienced identical extremes of heat: 100°.

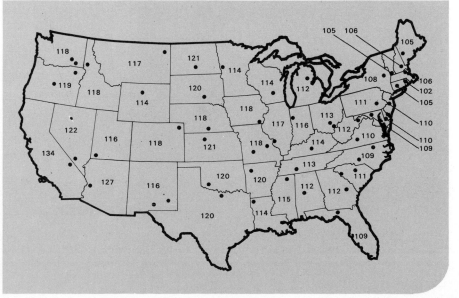

The Vocabulary of the Clouds

Long before meteorology became established as a science, man learned to read the storm in the gathering thunderhead, and see the promise of rain in a mackerel sky or in a halo around the moon. The various forms that clouds take are still among the most important indicators of future weather even for modern forecasters. But it was not until 150 years ago that weathermen began to formulate a scientific nomenclature to designate different types of clouds. The first useful cloud vocabulary was devised in 1803 by a part-time English meteorologist named Luke Howard, who identified three main types of clouds by their distinctive shapes and heights. He gave them the Latin names *cirrus* ("curl of hair"), *cumulus* ("pile") and *stratus* ("spread out"). From that beginning, meteorologists have classified the 10 cloud families which appear in the pictures below and on the opposite page. Each type, in its appearance, its altitude and its way of moving, usually foretells a particular kind of weather.

CIRRUS   *20,000 TO 40,000 FEET*

The delicate fibers of these clouds are usually white filaments composed of tiny ice crystals, sometimes with a silky sheen. They do not lead to rain themselves, but can often indicate the location of a distant storm, whose fringe winds may create conditions in which cirrus clouds form.

CIRROCUMULUS   *20,000 TO 40,000 FEET*

A thin sheet of white, cirrocumulus—the cloud of the mackerel sky—is composed of very small grains or ripples, sometimes merged, sometimes separate, but always more or less regularly arranged. A precursor of a warm front, it thickens at the approach of a storm into cirrostratus *(below, left)*.

CIRROSTRATUS   *20,000 TO 40,000 FEET*

A halo around the sun, which proverbially announces rain, looms above city chimney stacks. It is caused by the tiny ice crystals of cirrostratus, a whitish veil which is too thin to mask the outline of the sun. When this cloud thickens, proverb is likely to become fact—rainfall within 24 hours.

ALTOCUMULUS   *8,000 TO 20,000 FEET*

Composed of water droplets instead of the ice of cirrus clouds, altocumulus is a canopy of white or gray flakes, rounded masses and rolls. The cloud is sometimes a sign of rain, especially when some of its masses rise higher than their neighbors; they indicate possible thunderstorms.

ALTOSTRATUS *8,000 TO 20,000 FEET*

Although the sky is likely to be completely covered by this cloud, its fibrous sheet, which is roughly uniform in appearance, is thin enough to reveal the sun vaguely, as if seen through a ground glass. When altostratus increases, it may indicate rain or snow of a lasting and continuous nature.

NIMBOSTRATUS *BELOW 8,000 FEET*

Thick enough to blot the shape of the sun completely, nimbostratus disgorges continuous rain or snow, which gives it a diffuse appearance. In the life cycle of a storm, this cloud develops from altostratus that has descended closer to the earth. It is sometimes called simply "nimbus."

STRATOCUMULUS *BELOW 8,000 FEET*

A continuous canopy of irregular folds and layers interspersed with dark sheets or patches, stratocumulus is likely to form in the wake of a cold front which is overrunning an area. Stratocumulus is not usually a precipitation cloud, but occasionally may produce a light sprinkling of snow.

STRATUS *BELOW 8,000 FEET*

The lowest and most uniform-appearing of the clouds, stratus sometimes occurs when fog drifts over the warmed surface of the land and then rises. A flat gray cloud with a ceiling-like underside, it often yields drizzle or snow grains—very small particles of ice that fall in tiny quantities.

CUMULUS *BASE TO TOP: 8,000-45,000 FEET*

Dense and sharply outlined, cumulus clouds develop vertically in the form of billowing mounds and towers. Their tops shine brilliant-white in the sun, while their bases are often dark. Cumulus clouds do not bring rain unless they become extremely tall. Then they develop into cumulonimbus *(right)*.

CUMULONIMBUS *BASE TO TOP: 10,000-60,000 FEET*

Building over a summer landscape or a tropic sea, these clouds almost invariably bring thunderstorms and heavy rain; occasionally they produce hail. The tallest cumulonimbus thrust their heads into the cold upper air, and their tops assume the form of anvils, with trailing wisps of cirrus.

BIBLIOGRAPHY

General

Benstead, C.R., *The Weather Eye.* Robert Hale Ltd., 1954.

Blumenstock, David I., *The Ocean of Air.* Rutgers University Press, 1959.

*Cantzlaar, George L., *Your Guide to the Weather.* Barnes & Noble, 1964.

*Hare, Frederick Kenneth, *The Restless Atmosphere.* Hillary House, 1963.

†Holmes, David C., *The Story of Weather.* Pyramid Publications, 1963.

Humphreys, W. J., *Ways of the Weather.* Ronald Press, 1942.

Huschke, Ralph E., ed., *Glossary of Meteorology.* American Meteorological Society, 1959.

Kimble, George H. T., *Our American Weather.* McGraw-Hill, 1955.

*Lehr, Paul E., R. Will Burnett and Herbert S. Zim, *Weather.* Simon & Schuster, 1957.

*Longstreth, T. Morris, *Understanding the Weather.* Macmillan, 1953.

Murchie, Guy, *Song of the Sky.* Houghton Mifflin, 1954.

Pilkington, Roger, *The Ways of the Air.* Criterion Books, 1962.

*Spar, Jerome, *Earth, Sea and Air.* Addison-Wesley, 1962.

Sutton, O. G., *The Challenge of the Atmosphere.* Harper & Row, 1961. †*Understanding Weather.* Penguin Books, 1960.

History

Ludlum, David M., *Early American Hurricanes, 1492-1870.* American Meteorological Society, 1963.

Shaw, Sir Napier, *Manual of Meteorology, Vol. 1.* Cambridge University Press, 1926.

Sloane, Eric, *Folklore of American Weather.* Meredith Press, 1963.

Whitnah, Donald R., *A History of the United States Weather Bureau.* University of Illinois Press, 1961.

*Wolf, A., *A History of Science, Technology and Philosophy in the 16th and 17th Centuries* (2 vols.). Peter Smith, 1963. *A History of Science, Technology and Philosophy in the 18th Century* (2 vols.). Peter Smith, 1963.

Winds, Clouds and Rain

†Battan, Louis J., *Cloud Physics and Cloud Seeding.* Doubleday Anchor, 1962.

Brown, Slater, *World of the Wind.* Bobbs-Merrill, 1961.

Ludlam, F.H., and R.S. Scorer, *Cloud Study.* Macmillan, 1958.

*Mason, B.J., *Clouds, Rain and Rainmaking.* Cambridge University Press, 1962.

Storms

†Battan, Louis J., *The Nature of Violent Storms.* Doubleday Anchor, 1961. †*The Thunderstorm.* New American Library, 1964.

Dunn, Gordon E., and Banner I. Miller, *Atlantic Hurricanes.* Louisiana State University Press, 1964.

Flora, Snowden D., *Tornadoes of the United States.* University of Oklahoma Press, 1958.

Stewart, George R., *Storm.* Modern Library, 1947.

Sutton, Ann, and Myron, *Nature on the Rampage.* J. B. Lippincott, 1962.

Tannehill, Ivan Ray, *Hurricane Hunters.* Dodd, Mead, 1955.

Viemeister, Peter E., *The Lightning Book.* Doubleday, 1961.

Observing and Forecasting

Fisher, Robert Moore, *How about the Weather?* Harper & Row, 1958.

Middleton, W.E. Knowles, and Athelstan F. Spilhaus, *Meteorological Instruments.* University of Toronto Press, 1953.

Spilhaus, Athelstan F., *Weathercraft.* Viking Press, 1951.

Thompson, Philip D., *Numerical Weather Analysis and Prediction.* Macmillan, 1961.

*Available in paperback edition.
†Available only in paperback edition.

ACKNOWLEDGMENTS

The editors of this book are especially indebted to Professor James E. Miller, Chairman, Department of Meteorology and Oceanography, School of Engineering and Science, New York University, and to the following people and institutions: Dr. Filippo Affronti, Professor of Meteorology, University of Catania, Catania, Sicily; Mrs. Elizabeth Ashley, Office of Public Relations, American Meteorological Society, Boston, Mass.; Dr. Charles Atlas and staff, Weather Radar Branch, Meteorological Laboratory, Air Force Cambridge Research Laboratories, Sudbury, Mass.; Silvio Bedini, Curator, Division of Mechanical and Civil Engineering, Smithsonian Institution, Washington, D.C.; Dr. Harry Bober, Institute of Fine Arts, New York University; Dr. George P. Cressman, Director of National Meteorological Services, Herbert S. Lieb, Acting Director of Public Information and John C. Nyhan, Public Information Specialist, U.S. Weather Bureau, Washington, D.C.; Gordon E. Dunn, Director, and staff, National Hurricane Center, Miami, Fla.; Dr. Dave Fultz, Hydrodynamics Laboratory, Department of Geophysical Sciences, University of Chicago; Dr. R. Cecil Gentry, Director, Hurricane Research Laboratory, Miami, Fla.; Guy Gosselin, Chief Observer, Mount Washington Observatory, Mount Washington, Gorham, N.H.; George T. Hamilton, Manager, Pinkham Notch Camp, Appalachian Mountain Club, Gorham, N.H.; Dr. C.W. Hansell; Charles G. Knudsen, Meteorologist-in-Charge, Melvin Oppenheimer, Forecaster, and Gerald L. Shak, Supervising Forecaster, U.S. Weather Bureau, New York City; Dr. Helmut Landsberg, Director of Climatology, U.S. Weather Bureau, Washington, D.C.; Dr. David M. Ludlum, Editor, *Weatherwise,* Princeton, N.J.; Charles B. Moore, Arthur D. Little, Inc., Cambridge, Mass.; Dr. Vincent J. Schaefer, Professor of Atmospheric Science, State University of New York at Albany; Dr. Richard A. Schleusener, Associate Research Engineer, Foothills Campus, Colorado State University, Fort Collins, Colo.; Dr. Richard M. Schotland, Professor of Meteorology, School of Engineering and Science, New York University; Maynard E. Smith, Leader, Meteorology Group, Brookhaven National Laboratories; Kenneth C. Spengler, Executive Secretary, American Meteorological Society, Boston, Mass.; Research Flight Facility, U.S. Weather Bureau, Miami, Fla.; and 53rd Weather Reconnaissance Squadron, U.S.A.F., Savannah, Ga.

INDEX

Numerals in italics indicate a photograph or painting of the subject mentioned.

A

Abbe, Cleveland, 157
"Absolute zero," 36
Adams, John Quincy, 155
Air: Aristotle's concept of, 128; density of, 40; ionization, 113-114, 176, 190; movement of, 37, 39-41, 57, 85 (*see also* Air masses); water-vapor capacity of, 83. *See also* Atmosphere
Air conditioning, 121
Air masses: characteristics of, 41; and cyclone development, 136; defined, 41; effects on temperate-zone weather, 41-42, *74*, 75, 78; and fronts, 86-87, *94-97;* and heat transfer, 18, 41; source regions of, 41, *map* 75; symbols for, 41; types of, 41, 75
Air pollution, *74*, 75, *119*, 178; control, 179. *See also* Smog
Air pressure. *See* Atmospheric pressure
Airplanes, weather observation by, 82, *149*, 158, *175*. *See also* Hurricane hunters
Alaskan glacier, *32-33*
Alps, 60, 61, 85
Altocumulus clouds, 86, *97*, *194*
Altostratus clouds, 86, *97*, *195*
Amazon basin, 100
Anemometer, 58-59; homemade, *161*, *164-165*
Aneroid barometer, *170*
Animals, effect of weather on, 112
Anticyclones, 59, 64-65
Antitrade winds, 63
Apeliotes, wind, *59*
Appalachians, 9-10, 15
Arctic, weather-improvement schemes for, 178-180
Aristotle, 58, 81, 128, 142, 153-154
Atlantic coast, hurricanes, *30-31*, 44, *map* 54, 133-134
Atlantic Ocean: area of origin of hurricanes, 42, 44, *map* 54, 65; winds and trade routes, *map* 63
Atmosphere, 13-15, 16, 127; absorption of solar energy, 12, 35-36, 38; composition of, 14; general circulation of, 62-64, 68-71; "greenhouse" effect of, 38; heat exchange in, 18, 39, *40*, 41, 68, *69*, 90; impurities in, as condensation nuclei, 84, 88; layers of, 14, *15;* origin of word, 11; research models of, 173-175; temperatures in, 14, *graph* 15; water content of, 14; water vapor in, 14, 21, 36, 38, 39; weight of, 13, 35. *See also* Air
Atmospheric electricity and lightning, *104;* and rain, 87, *103*. *See also* Ionization
Atmospheric (barometric) pressure, 13-14; change of, with altitude, 14, 144; defined, 39-40; effects on man's physical and mental condition, 110, 111-113, 114; high *vs.* low, global belts, *map* 69; imbalances, and movement of air, 39-41, 57; indication on weather maps, *168;* laws governing, 130-131; measuring, *128*, *142*, 144, *154*, *166-167;* units of, 168; upper air, measuring, 59, 144, 145, *149-151*, 158; and weather forecasting, 58, 154-155, *table* 167
Auroras, 176

B

Baguio, hurricane, 42
Balaklava, fleet disaster of, *146-147*, 156
Balkans, bora of, 61
Balloons, weather surveillance by, 10, 59, 82, *149-151*, 158, *175*, 178, *182*, 183; early, *134*, *144-145;* instrument panel, *135;* Operation Skyhook 60, *177*
Barometers, *135*, *142*, 154-155, *170;* homemade, *166-167;* Hooke's wheel barometer, *154;* Torricelli's, *128*, 142, 154
Barometric pressure. *See* Atmospheric pressure
Bartholomaeus Anglicus, 57
Baseball, financial losses from rain, *91*
Beaufort, Admiral Sir Francis, 165
Beaufort scale of wind velocity, *table* 164, 165
Behavior, human, effect of weather on, 110-114
Bergen (Norway) School of Meteorology, 135-136, *148*
Bergeron, Tor, 88
Bergeron-Findeisen theory of rain, 88-90
Bering Strait, proposed damming of, 179
Bermuda, rainstorm, 16, *17*
Bjerknes, Jakob, 136, *148*
Bjerknes, Vilhelm, 135-136, 137, *148*
Blanchard, Jean Pierre, *144*
Blizzards, 26, 65; Donner Pass, *99*, 108
Body, human, effects of weather on, 9, 109, 111-114; medieval chart, *139*
Book of Signs, Theophrastus, 154
Bora, wind, 61
Boreas, wind, *58*
Boyle, Robert, 130, *131*, 138
Boyle's Law of gases, 130
Brahe, Tycho, 129
Bush, Vannevar, 180

C

"Caloric" theory of heat, 37-38
Carbon dioxide, in air, 14; absorption of solar radiation by, 36; industrial waste, annual amount and effects, 178; and positive ions, 113
Carbon dioxide, solid, use in cloud-seeding, 89 90, *102*
Carbon-dust layer, on Arctic ice, 178-179
Caribbean, area of origin of hurricanes, 42, 44, *map* 54
"Cauliflower" clouds, 85
Charles, Jacques, 130, *131*, 144
Charles's Law of gases, 130
Chicago World's Fair of 1893, weather forecasts for, *159*
China: ancient weather gods, *140-141;* monsoon, 62, *map* 73; primitive weather instruments, 58
Chinook, wind, 61, 85
Cirrocumulus clouds, *87*, *97*, *194*
Cirrostratus clouds, 85, 86, *97*, *194*
Cirrus clouds, 84-85, *86*, *96*, *97*, *194*, 195; streamers, *77*
Cities: effect on weather, *60*, 87, *118*, 119, 178; air pollution, *74*, 75, *119*, 178
City of San Francisco (train), *99*, 108
Clausewitz, Karl von, 108
Climate Makes the Man, Mills, 110
Cloud cover, weather-map symbols for, *table* 168
Cloud droplets, 38, 39, 82, 84; forming of, 84, 92, 102-103; forming of precipitation from, 87-90, 92, 102; supercooled, 88
Cloud maps, global, 82
Cloud-seeding, 50, 89-90, *124;* in laboratory, *102*, 103
"Cloud societies," 184
Clouds, 81-82, 84-87, *194-195;* absorption of radiant heat by, 38; as aid in weather forecasting, 81, 86-87, *194-195;* altitude of, measuring, 82; anatomy of, 188; Aristotle's concept of, 128; classification and nomenclature of, 84-85, *194-195;* folklore of, 81; forming of, 39, 84, 85-87; in frontal activity, 86-87, *94-97*, 188; good weather, 87; of ice crystals, 85, *86*, *96*, *194;* and jet streams, *77;* orographic (mountain-bred), 16, 85, *87*, *98;* and precipitation, 87-90; rainstorm, *17*, 87; reflection of solar energy by, 36; research, 82, 173, *188-189;* space views of, *34*, *51*, 82, 176, 177, 184, 188; speed measurements, 82, 173, *189;* thunderstorm, *22-23*, 85, *86*, 87, 89, *94-95*, *100-101*, *104*, *194*, *195;* various types, *86-87;* weight of water vapor in, 35, 87
Coastal weather features, 15, 59-60, *72*
Cold front, 86-87, *94-95*, 195; and squall line, *22-23;* defined, 86, *table* 168; symbol for, *table* 168; weather sequence of, 86-87
Columbus, Christopher, 63
Computers, electronic, use in weather forecasting, 10, 127, 137-138, *150*, *152*, 153, 158, 159, 160, 177, 186, *187;* curve plotting, 153, *181;* IBM card, *137;* mathematical model of atmosphere, 174-175; tracking of storms, 50, *187*
Condensation, *20-21*, 39, 81-84, *85*, 90, *92-93*, *102-103;* main cause of, 83; process of, 84; relationship to relative humidity, *85*. *See also* Clouds; Dew; Fog; Frost; Precipitation
Condensation nuclei, 21, 84, 92-93, 190
Connecticut River, 1955 flooding, 26
Conservation Laws: of Energy, 131; of Mass, 131
Constellation, schooner, *67*
Continental air masses, 41, *map* 75; polar, *74-75*
Convection, thermal, 39-40; and condensation and cloud formation, 81, 85, 87, *94*, *100;* global belts, 62-64, 68, *69;* large-scale, 24, 40, 62-64, 132; local, small-scale, 40, 59, *60*, 87; over man-made "hot spots," *60*, 87, 119, 178
Convective storm, *94*
Copernicus, Nicholas, 128
Coriolis, Gaspard Gustave de, 63, 70
Coriolis force, 52, 63, 64, *70-71*, 133
Crime rate, effect of weather on, *graph* 110
Cumulonimbus clouds, 85, *86*, 87, *195;* updrafts and downdrafts of, 87, 89. *See also* Thunderheads
Cumulus clouds, 84-85, 87, *94*, *100*, 194, *195*
Cup anemometer, 58; homemade, *161*, *164-165*
Curve plotter, automatic, 153, *181*
Cusa, Nicolaus de, 129
Cyclones, 59, 64-65; development of (polar-front theory), 136; effects on mental and physical health, 111, 114; tropical, 42, 65 (*See also* Hurricanes; Typhoons); west-east movement of, 156

D

Dalton, John, 130-131
Dalton's Law of Partial Pressures, 130-131
Dampier, William, 133
Data plotter, automatic, 153, *181*
Datoo, wind, 60
Death Valley, California, rainfall, 83
Deserts, *28-29*, *98;* lack of rain, 83, 85; latitudes, 63
Dew, *20*, 21, 82, 83
Dew point, 83, 84
Dexter, O. E., 110
Discomfort index, *graph* 84
"Doctor," wind, 60
Doldrums, 63, *map* 69, 100-101; Halley's map, *132*
Donner party, 108
Donner Pass, *City of San Francisco* in, *99*, 108
Doppler radars, 189
Downdrafts, *60*, 87, 89, *95*
Drainage wind, 61
Drake, Sir Francis, 107
Drizzle, 75, 195
Drought, *28-29*. *See also* Deserts; Dust Bowl; Dust storms
Dry ice, use of in cloud-seeding, 89-90, *102*
Duckworth, Joseph P., 49
Dust, in air: absorption of solar radiation by, 36; as condensation nuclei, 84
Dust storms, *28*, 29, 35

E

Earth, 12-13, *68-69;* amount of solar radiation received, 11-12, 36; distance from sun, 11, 36; rotation of, and its effects on weather, 12, 40, 52, 62-64, *70-71*, 132-133; shape of, and its effect on weather, 13; tilt of, and its effect on seasons, *12*, 13
"Earthshine," in space views of earth, 36
Easterlies, winds, 52, *70-71;* polar, 64, 136
Egmont, H.M.S., in hurricane, *65*
Egypt, 29; primitive weather instruments, 58
Eisenhower, Dwight D., 109
Electricity. *See* Atmospheric electricity; Ionization
Electromagnetic radiation, 12
Emotions, effect of weather on, 9, 110-114
Energy, Law of Conservation of, 131
Energy, potential *vs.* kinetic, 131. *See also* Heat transfer
Environmental Science Services Administration (ESSA), 157, 174
Equatorial regions: and atmospheric heat exchange, 38-39, *40*, 41, 62-63, 68, *69;* lack of weather stations, *182-183;* rain, *map* 82, 87-88, *100-101;* wind cell of, 62-63, 68, *69-71*. *See also* Tropics
Equinoxes (spring and autumn), *12-13*
Eskimos, protection from cold, 122
Espy, James P., 81, 103, 156
Evaporation, 39; control of, 179; energy consumption in, 90; Gulf of Mexico, 35; latent heat of, 39; and precipitation, cycle, 16, 82, 90; total annual amount, 82, 90
Exosphere, 176

F

Fair-weather indications, 65, 87, 154, *table* 167, *171*
Fall wind, 61
Feather River, California, flooding, *27*
Findeisen, Walter, 88
Flash floods, 26
Flies, bites of, and weather lore, 154
Flood forecasts, 159
Floods, river, 10, *26-27*
Florence, Academy of Experiments of, *39*, *142*
Fog, *20-21*, 75, 178, 195; formation of, 84; ground fog, 84, *116-117;* laser-beam examinations of, 173, 188; in London, 1952, casualties, 107; weather-map symbol for, *table* 168
Föhn, wind, 61, 85, 111
Föhn wall, 85
Folklore of weather, 10, 81, 154
Forecasting. *See* Weather forecasting
France, mistral of, 61
Franklin, Benjamin, 127, 133-134, 155
Friction, between atmosphere and surface of earth, 62-63, 174, 175
Front(s): cold *vs.* warm, 86; cyclone development at, 136; defined, 86, 136; tracking of movement of, 169, 188; types of, *table* 168; weather activity, 86-87, *94-97;* weather-map symbols for, *table* 168
Frontal thunderstorm, 87, 94, *95*
Frost, *20*, 21, 82, 83, *85*
Frost prevention, *124*, 125
Fumarea, 61

G

Gale, wind speed, *table* 164
Galileo Galilei, 37, 39, 129, 142
Galveston, Texas, 1900 hurricane, 54
Gases, laws of, 130-131
Gathman, Louis, 103
Gay-Lussac, Joseph, 130
General Gas Law, 130
Glacier, *32-33*
Glaisher, James, 135, 144, *145*
Glaze, *92-93*
Gods of weather, 138, *140-141*, 153
Great Plains, 15
Greece, ancient: knowledge of weather, *58-59*, 81, 128, 138, 153-154; weather gods, *141*, 153
"Greenhouse" effect of atmosphere, 38

H

Haboob, wind, 29
Hadley, George, 63, 132-133
Hadley cell, 63
Hail, 82, 89, *92-93*, 195
Hailstorms, control of, 124, *179*
Hair hygrometer, 142, *143*, *162-163*
Halley, Edmund, 132, 133
Hannibal, 108
Hanov, Michael Christoph, 58
Hansell, C. W., 113-114
Harris, Henry, *149*
Haze, *74*
Health, effect of weather on, 109, 111-114
Heat: conversion from solar energy, 12, 35, 36; defined, 36, 38; and First Law of Thermodynamics, 131; global system of exchange of, 39, *40*, 41, 62-64, 68, *69;* history of study of, 37-38; latent, in air's water vapor, 39; radiant, 36; as source of all weather, 38-39
Heat transfer, 18, 31, *diagram* 40, 69
Helmholtz, Hermann von, 131, 132
Henry, Joseph, 146, 156
Hexadecanol, evaporation control by, 179
High pressure: anticyclonic systems, 65; belts, *map* 69; indication of systems on weather maps, *168;* weather characteristics, 65, 154-155, 167
History, examples of effect of weather on course of, 107, 108-109
History of meteorology, 127-138, *139-151*, 153-160
Hooke, Robert, 129, 154, 155
Horrocks, Jeremiah, 129
Horse latitudes, 63, *map* 69, *71*
Howard, Luke, 84, 194
Humidity, 75; effect on human behavior, 110, 111; measuring, 129, 142, *143*, *155*,

162-163; in tropics, 100; upper air, measuring, 59, 144, 149-151, 158. See also Relative humidity
Huntington, Ellsworth, 110, 112
Hurricane, Great, of 1780, 65
Hurricane Cleo (1964), 44-45, 51
Hurricane Connie (1955), 44
Hurricane Diane (1955), 44
Hurricane Donna (1960), 107-108
Hurricane hunters, 44, 46-47, 49
Hurricanes, 30-31, 43, 59, 65, 66; annual number of, 65; areas of origin, 42, map 54; casualties from, 42, 54; conditions for development of, 41, 42, diagrams 52, 53; control of, 50; damage by, 42, 54-55; death of, diagram 52; early observations of (Franklin, Redfield), 133-134; energy release, 35; eye of, 48-49; at Jamestown (1667), 107; origin of name, 65; paths of, map 54; structure of, 52-53; tracking and warning, 44-51, 172, 176, 186; weather map symbol for, table 168; wind force, 42, table 164
Hurricanes Dora, Ethel, Florence (1964), 51
Hyderabad, Pakistan, wind scoops of, 120-121
Hydrologic cycle, 82
Hygrometer, 155, 170; early, 39, 142, 143; homemade, 162-163
Hygroscope, Hooke's, 129, 155

I

Ice age, 32
Ice-crystal clouds, 85, 86, 96-97, 194; proposed man-made, over Arctic, 179
Ice-crystal theory of precipitation, 88-90
Ice crystals in atmosphere and clouds, 14, 88, 92, 96, 104, 190; detection of, 173
Icebergs, 32
Illnesses, weather-induced, 109, 111-114
Imbat, wind, 60
India, monsoons of, 24-25, 62, 72, map 73
Infrared radiation, 12, 36, 38, 39, 177; wavelength, 12
Insolation (incoming solar radiation), 12
Institute for Advanced Study, Princeton, computer-meteorology team at, 138, 150
Instruments, meteorological, 10, 128; amateur weather station, 161-167; ancient, 58, 142, 143, 154; basic, 37, 39, 58, 129, 130, 142-143, 154, 155; hurricane-hunter plane's instrument panel, 46-47; recent developments, 173-178; for upper-air observation, 10, 59, 149-151, 173, 175-178, 190-191; weather-balloon instrument panel, 135
Insulation, 122
International cooperation in meteorology, 155, 158, 160, 175, 182. See also World Meteorological Organization
International Geophysical Year (IGY), 175
International Years of the Quiet Sun, 175
Inter-tropical convergence zone, 63, 100-101
Ionization, of air, 113; caused by solar phenomena, 176, 190; and lightning, 104; measuring, 190-191
Ionosphere, exploration of, 175-176
Ions: described, 113; effect of imbalances on human body, 113-114
Isobars, 168

J

Jacksonville, Florida, hurricane damage, 54-55
Jamestown, 1667 hurricane, 107
Japan: Kublai Khan's invasion of, 109; monsoon, 62
Jefferson, Thomas, 155
Jeffries, John, 144
Jet streams, 35, 64, 76-77, 175
Johnson, Lyndon B., 160
Joule, James, 38, 131

K

Kamikaze (China Sea typhoon), 109
Kapalilua, wind, 60
Kepler, Johannes, 129
Kinetic energy, 131
Kircher, Athanasius, 13
Kornblueh, Igho, 113-114
Kraft, Ray, 50
Krueger, Albert P., 113

L

Lambert, Johann Heinrich, 157
Laminated cloud, 87
Land: heat absorption and retention of,

15, 59-60, 62, 72; share of total evaporation and precipitation, 82
Land breeze, 15, 40, 59-60, 72
Landform, effect on weather, 11, 15-16, 40, 60-61, 71, 72, 85, 87, 98
Lange, Karl, 149
Langmuir, Irving, 89
Lapham, Increase, 157
Laser, 173, 177, 180, 188-189
Latent heat, 39
Lawrence, T. E., 29
Lesser Antilles, area of origin of hurricanes, map 54
Levanter, wind, 111
Ligda, Myron, 184
Light, 12, 36, 178; wavelength, 12
Lightning, 104-105; Aristotle's concept of, 128; fatal experiment, 126
London: 1952 fog casualties, 107; smog, 178
Loomis, Elias, 156
Los Angeles smog, 178, 179
Low pressure: belts, maps 69, 100-101; cyclonic systems, 64-65; indication of systems on weather maps, 168; weather characteristics, 65, 154-155, 167

M

Mackerel sky, 194
McKinley, William, 44
Madison, James, 155
Mainsprings of Civilization, Huntington, 110
Man, effects of weather on, 9, 109-114; medieval chart, 139
MANIAC computer, 127, 137-138, 150
Marine weather stations, 157, 172, 178, 183
Maritime air masses, 41, map 75; tropical, 74
Mass, Law of Conservation of, 131
Mathematics, use in meteorology, 127, 135, 137-138, 150; numerical model of atmosphere, 174-175
Mead, Lake, Nevada, sandstorm at, 116
Mental effects of weather, 9, 110-114
Mesosphere, graph 15; exploration of, 175-176
Meteoric dust, 175, 190
Meteorograph, 149
Meteorologica, Aristotle, 128-129, 142, 154
Meteorology, 10, 38; annual federal spending on, 10; defined, 127; emerges as science, 135, 138; future of, 180; history of, 127-138, 139-151, 153-160; origin of term, 10, 142; problems of, 127
Mexico, Gulf of: area of origin of hurricanes, map 54; evaporation rate, 35; source of saturated air, 80
Microweather, 114, 115-123; in cities, 118-119; control, 119, 121, 124-125
Midwest, U.S.: floods, 26; rain, 80; tornadoes, 78
Millibar, unit, 168
Mills, Clarence A., 110, 111-112
Minerva, weather balloon, 134
Mississippi Valley, 15
Mistral, wind, 61
Models of atmospheric processes, 173-175
Molecular motion, 36, 38. See also Heat
Monsoon, 24-25, 61-62, 72, 73, 132; effect on human behavior, 110; origin of term, 61
Montgolfier brothers, 144
Moon, halo around, 194
Morse, Samuel F. B., 156
Motion, Newton's Second Law of, 129-130
Mountain ranges, effect on weather, 15-16, 60-61, 85, 87, 98
Mountain (thermal slope) wind, 40, 59, 60
Mythology of weather, 138, 140-141, 153

N

Nacreous clouds, 86
Napoleon Bonaparte, 108
NASA, 59, 177
National Bureau of Standards, 189
National Hurricane Center, 44-47
National Meteorological Center (NMC), 153, 158, 186
National Science Foundation, 177
National Weather Service, 147
Nephoscope, 169
New England, 1955 flood, 26
New York City, 74
Newton, Sir Isaac, 13, 129-130, 131, 132, 138
Nile River, annual flooding, 26
Nimbostratus clouds, 85, 86, 97, 195
Nimbus clouds. See Nimbostratus clouds
Nimbus weather satellite, 59, 51, 175, 177, 182, 183, 184-185; orbit of, 176; photographs taken by, 51, 177, 186

Nitrogen, in air, 14, 38
Noctilucent clouds, 86
NOMAD weather station, 172, 183
Normandy, 1944 invasion of, 109
Norsemen, weather gods of, 141
Notos, wind, 58
Numerical forecasting, 136, 137-138, 150, 152, 153, 174-175, 186, 187

O

Occluded front, table 168
Ocean currents, 57; effect of earth rotation on, 12
Oceans: possible rise of level, 178; share of total evaporation and precipitation, 82; vital role in weather, 15, 38; weather surveillance, 157, 158, 172, 176, 178
Olmsted, Denison, 134
Oppenheimer, Mel, 169
Orographic clouds, 16, 85, 87, 98
Orographic wind, 16, 61, 85, 98
Overlord, Operation, 109
Oxygen, in air, 14, 38; and negative ions, 113
Ozone, in air: absorption of solar radiation by, 36; effect on temperature, graph 15
Ozone layers, 175

P

Pacific Northwest, rainfall, 83, 98
Pacific Ocean: space-flight view of, 34; typhoons, 65, 133
Paris, France, rainstorm, 118
Partial Pressures, Dalton's Law of, 130-131
Pascal, Blaise, 144
Périer, Florin, 144
Philosophiae Naturalis Principia Mathematica, Newton, 129-130, 132
Physical effects of weather on man, 9, 109, 111-114
Pilot balloons, 59
Plateaus, winds from, 61
Plutarch, 81
Polar air masses, 41, map 75, 86; continental, 74
Polar easterlies, 64, 70, 136
Polar-front theory, 136, 148
Polar regions, 18, 19; and atmospheric heat exchange, 39, 40, 41, 62-63, 64, 68, 69; lack of weather stations, 183; wind cells, 64, 68, 69-71
Pollution. See Air pollution
Ponente, wind, 60
Pool, heated outdoor, 123
Post, C. W., 81
Potential energy, 131
Precipitation, 14, 81-83, 87-90, 91-105; Aristotle's concept of, 128; causes of, 87-89, 189; defined, 82; energy release, 39; and evaporation cycle, 16, 90; in frontal activity, 86, 87, 94, 95, 96, 97; indication on weather maps, 168; kinds of, 89, 92-93; laser and radar research, 188, 189; total annual amount, 82. See also Hail; Rain; Sleet; Snow
Pressure. See Atmospheric pressure
Pressure systems, 64-65; movement of, 168. See also High pressure; Low pressure
Prevailing westerlies. See Westerlies
Princeton, battle of (1777), 109
Princeton, Institute for Advanced Study, computer-meteorology team at, 138, 150
Principia Mathematica, Newton, 129-130, 132
Proenza, Xavier, 50
Provincetown, Massachusetts, storm waves at, 30-31
Psychrometer, 162-163

R

Radar, use in weather surveillance, 59, 82, 107, 177, 180, 182-183, 188, 189-191
Radar stations, weather surveillance, 11, 157, 190-191
Radarscope: Doppler scopes, 189; hurricane tracking, 45, 46-47
Radiant heat, 36, 38
Radiation: electromagnetic, 12; infrared, 12, 36, 38, 39, 177; terrestrial, 12, 36; ultraviolet, 12, 175, 178; X-rays, 175. See also Solar radiation
Radiosonde, 59, 150-151, 158
Rain, 80, 91; annual averages, 82-83; Bergeron-Findeisen theory of, 88-90; causes of, 87-89, 92-93, 189; clouds, 17, 86, 87, 195; conjectures on increase of, through warfare, 81; daily amount of, 90; energy release, 39; in frontal activity, 23, 86, 87, 94, 95, 96, 97; global distribution of, map 82; in-

creased fall over cities, 118, 178; orographic, 16, 98; radar research, 188, 189; signs of coming, 65, 86-87, 154, 162, table 167, 194, 195; in temperate zones, 88-89; total annual amount, 82; tropical, 87-88, 100-101; weather-map symbols for, table 168
Rain forest, tropical, 100-101
Rain gauges, 129, 142, 154
Rainbands, hurricane, 52-53
Raindrops: forming of, 87-90, 92-93, 103; radar measurements of, 189; shape of, 102
Rainmaking, 89, 90, 103, 124
Rainstorms, 17, 65, 87; compared to thunderstorm, 104; and flooding, 26-27
Rawinsonde, 59
Redfield, William C., 134
Relative humidity, chart 163; and condensation, 85; defined, 162; and discomfort index, graph 84; measuring, 162-163
Richardson, Lewis Fry, 136, 137, 138, 153
Richmann, Georg Wilhelm, 126
Rivers, flooding of, 10, 26-27
Riviera, French, 15
"Roaring forties," 64
Robertson, Etienne 134
Rockets, weather surveillance by, 10, 59, 175-176
Rocky Mountains, 15, 85
Rossby, Carl-Gustaf, 148-149
Royal Society (of London), 155
Ruggles, Daniel, rainmaking device of, 89
Rumford, Count (Benjamin Thompson), 37-38
Ruskin, John, 147

S

Sacramento Valley, 15
Sahara, 28-29
St. Louis, smog, 119
Salt particles, in air, 84, 88, 92
San Francisco, 15
Sandstorms, 29, 116
Satellites, meteorological. See Weather satellites
Saussure, Horace Bénédict de, 142, 143
Sayre, Daniel, 149
Schaefer, Vincent J., 89, 103
Sea breeze, 15, 40, 59-60, 72
Seasons, cause of, 12, 13
Shamal, wind, 29
Shaw, Sir Napier, 153
Ships, weather reporting by, 11, 158
Sierra Nevada, 85, 99, 108; scheme to blast gaps in, 179
Silver iodide, use in weather control, 50, 89-90, 124
Sims, John, and his amateur weather station, 160, 161-171
Sirocco, wind, 111
Sky, explanation of blue tint of, 36
Skyhook 60, Operation, 177
Slave trade, Atlantic shipping routes, map 63
Sleet, 82, 89, 92
Smithsonian Institution, 146, 156, 157
Smog, 119, 178; control of, 179; and ion imbalance, 113
Snow, 82, 88-89, 106, 107; clouds, 195; energy release, 39; laboratory production of, 102, 103; radar research, 189; weather-map symbol for, table 168
Snow eater, wind, 98
Snowdrifts, 117, 119
Snowflakes, 92-93; forming of, 88-89; radar measurements of, 189
Solar flares, 176
Solar radiation, 11-12, diagrams 36; absorption by atmosphere and earth, 36; amount received by earth's atmosphere, 11-12, 36; and annual seasonal cycle, 12-13; conversion into heat, 12, 35, 36; loss by reflection, 36; nature of, 12; as power source for weather satellites, 184; during sunspot periods, 190
Solar system, 129
Solar weather, 175, 176
Solstices (summer and winter), 12-13
Southwest, U.S., 75
Space views of earth, 34, 51, 186; "earthshine," 36
Space weather research, 175-176, 190
Squall line, 22-23
Stationary front, table 168
Stewart, George, 107
Storm control, 50, 124, 179
Stormfury, Project, 50
Storms, 16, 17, 22-23; detection and warnings, 44-51, 159, 172, 176, 177; effects of approach of, on animals and humans, 112; release of excess energy by, 31. See also Blizzards; Hurricanes; Rainstorms; Thunderstorms; Tornadoes; Typhoons
Strabo, 61

198

Stratocumulus clouds, 85, *195*
Stratosphere, *graph* 15; exploration of, *149, 175-176, 177,* 178
Stratus clouds, 84-85, 194, *195*
Subtropics: land and sea breezes of, 60; trade winds of, 62
Suicide rate, effect of weather on, 110, 111
Sun, 11-12, *68;* distance from earth, 11, 36; halo around, *96,* 154, *194. See also* Solar radiation; Solar weather
Sunrise, *8;* red, and weather outlook, 154
Sunset, *18;* red, and weather outlook, 154, *171*
Sunspots, and ionization, 190
Suomi, Verner E., 177
Supercooling, 88
Symbols, meteorological, 41, *table* 168, 169; 18th Century, *157*

T

Taft, William Howard, 42
Taku Glacier, Alaska, *32-33*
Telegraphic weather-reporting networks, early, *146-147,* 156-157
Temperate zones: land and sea breezes of, 60; major weather features of, 41-42, 64-65; rain, 88-89. *See also* United States
Temperature: atmospheric, variances, 14, *graph* 15; average terrestrial, 39; in cities, 178; and condensation, 83, *85;* effect of shape of earth on, 13; effect on human behavior, 110-111; global extremes, *18-19;* extremes in U.S., *map* 193; imbalances, and movement of air, 39-41, 57, 62-64; indication on weather maps, *168;* low readings, 64; measuring, 37, 39, 129, *162-163;* possible rise of terrestrial, 178; in tropics, 100; upper air, measuring, 59, 144, 145, *149-151,* 158, 178
Temperature-humidity index, *graph* 84
Temperature inversion, 119
Terrestrial radiation, 12, 36
Texas, dust storm, *28*
Theophrastus, 81, 154
Thermal slope winds, 60
Thermodynamics, First Law of, 131
Thermometers, 37, *39,* 135, 142, 155, *162-163*
Thermoscope, 37
Thermosphere, *graph* 15
Thompson, Benjamin. *See* Rumford, Count
Thunder, Aristotle's concept of, 128
Thunderheads, 85, *86, 94-95, 101, 104*
Thunderstorms, *22-23, 104-105;* balloon-observation of, 134-135; clouds, 85, *86,* 87, 89, *94-95, 100-101, 194, 195;* convective, *94;* daily global number of, 35; development of, 104; energy released by, 35; frontal, 87, 94, *95;* weather-map symbol for, *table* 168
Tiros weather satellites, 50, 82, *175,* 176-177, *183,* 184
Tornadoes, 59, 65-66, *78-79;* cause, 78; origin of name, 65; research model of, 174; top wind speed, 66, 78; watch for, 10
Torricelli, Evangelista, *39,* 129; his barometer, *128,* 142, 154
"Tower of the Winds," Athenian, *58*
Towneley, Richard, 129
Trade winds, 52, 62-63, 66, *71,* 132-133; and Atlantic trade, *map* 63; Halley's map, *132*
Trans-mountain wind, 61, 85, *98*
Tropical air masses, 41, *map* 75, 78, 86; maritime, *74,* 76
Tropical cyclones, 42, 65. *See also* Hurricanes; Typhoons
Tropical rains, 87-88, *100-101;* belt, *map* 82, *map* 100-101
Tropics: land and sea breezes of, 60; mechanics of weather in, *diagram* 100; trade winds and doldrums of, 62-63, *drawing* 69, 70-71; *map* 132. *See also* Equatorial regions
Troposphere, 14-15; temperature of, *graph* 15; upper, exploration of, 176, 178
Turbulence, clear-air, 173
Twain, Mark, 42
Typhoons, 42, 65; computer record of, *187;* first description of, 133; weather-satellite photographs of, 51. *See also* Hurricanes

U

Ultraviolet radiation, 12, 175, 178; wavelength, 12
Umbrella, history of, *88*
United Nations. *See* World Meteorological Organization
United States: federal spending on meteorology, 10, 157; history of weather observation and forecasting, 155, 156-159; jet streams over, 76; major weather features of, 15, 41-42, 64-65, *map* 75, 86-87; movement of major weather systems, 168; rainfall, statistics, 83; temperature extremes, *map* 193; tornadoes of, 65-66, 78
University of Chicago, 173, 177
University of Pennsylvania School of Medicine, 112, 113
Updrafts, *60,* 62, 87, 89
Upper-air weather surveillance, 10-11, 59, *144-145, 149-151,* 157-158, 173, *175-177,* 178, *190-191. See also* Balloons; Rockets; Weather satellites
U.S. Air Force, 59, *189;* hurricane tracking, *map* 44-45
U.S. Navy, 177; hurricane tracking, *map* 44-45, *172*
U.S. Weather Bureau, 42, 58, 59, 153, 157-159, 174; beginnings of, 147, 157; budget, 157, 160; forecasts of, 158-159; functions of, 158; hurricane tracking, *44-47, 50-51, 186;* operation of, 157-159; reporting system of, sources of information, *10-11,* 157, 158, *map* 182-183; staff, 157, 160; weather maps of, *168,* 169

V

Valley wind, 40, 59, 60-61
Vanguard II satellite, *175*
Vent du Midi, 111
Vernal equinox, winds, *56*
Virazón, wind, 60
Viviani, Vincenzio, *39*
Von Neumann, John, 127, 137-138, *150,* 153
Vonnegut, Bernard, *102*

W

Waialeale, Mount, Hawaii, 83
Warfare: effects of weather on, 108-109; and rain, conjectures on relation between, 81
Warm front, 86; clouds, 86, *96-97,* 194; defined, 86, *table* 168; symbol for, *table* 168; weather sequence, 86
Washington, George, 109, 155
Washington, Mount, New Hampshire: cloudcap, 85; ski slope, *117*
Water: amount involved in evaporation-and-condensation cycle, 82, 90; in atmosphere, 14; global, possible rise of level of, 178; heat absorption and retention of, 15, 59-60, 62, 72; supercooled, 88
Water droplets, in air, 14, 39. *See also* Cloud droplets
Water vapor, in air, 14, 21, 81; absorption of radiant heat by, 12, 38; absorption of solar radiation by, 36; calculation of, 131; capacity of air for, 83; condensation of, *20-21,* 39, 81-84, *85,* 92-93; cooling of, 39, 83; and "greenhouse" effect, 38; latent heat energy of, 39; weight of, in cloud, 35, 87
Wave clouds, *87*
Weather buoys, *172, 183*
Weather changes. *See* Changes in weather
Weather-clock, 129
Weather control and modification, 119, 121, *124-125,* 173, 175, 178-180; cloud-seeding, 89-90, *102,* 103, *124;* evaporation control, 131; frost prevention, *124, 125;* hail prevention, 124, *179;* heat-trapping schemes for Arctic, 178-180; rainmaking, 89, 90, 103, *124;* smog prevention, 179; storm reduction, 50, 124, 179
Weather forecasting, 10-11, 96, 127, 153-160, 162, 169, 170, 182; accuracy of, 153, 159-160, 175, 178, 180; and barometric readings, 58, 154-155, *table* 167; cloud formations as aid in, 81, 86-87, *194-195;* folk art, 10, 154; of future, 177-178; history of, 127-128, 135-138, *146-151,* 153-157; long-range, 159, 174-175, 180; numerical, *136,* 137-138, *150, 152,* 153, 174-175, 186, *187;* wind as aid
in, 57-58, *table* 167. *See also* Instruments; Upper-air weather surveillance; Weather stations
Weather Forecasting, U.S. Weather Bureau, 58
Weather glass, 154
Weather maps, *168,* 169; automatic plotting of, 153, *181;* early, 146, *147,* 156; symbols, 41, *table* 168, 169
Weather Prediction by Numerical Process, Richardson, *136,* 137, 138
Weather records, early, 155-156
Weather satellites, 10, 50, *51,* 82, *175,* 176-177, 180, *182-185;* photographs taken by, *50, 51,* 176-177, 184, *186,* 187, 188; receiver for pictures of, *184*
Weather stations, 153, 157, 158, *172;* amateur, *161-167, 170-171;* automatic, *172,* 177-178, 180; global distribution, *map* 182-183; types of, *10-11*
Weather vanes. *See* Wind vanes
Westerlies, prevailing, 63-64, *70-71,* 98; and Atlantic trade, *map* 63
Wet-and-dry-bulb thermometer, *162-163*
Wheel barometer, *154*
Wilkes Station, Antarctica, 114, *115*
Willy-willy, wind, 42
Wind(s), 57-66, *67-79;* as aid in weather forecasting, 57-58, *table* 167; of air masses, 75; Aristotle's concepts of, *58-59,* 128; basic categories, 59; Beaufort scale of velocities, *table* 164, 165; cause of, 37, 39-40; cells, global, *68, 69, 70-71;* defined, 57; deflection of, by earth rotation, 12, 40, 52, 62-64, *70-71,* 132-133; of drought, *28-29;* effect on human behavior, 111, 114; energy of, 57; episodic, 59, 62-64, 66, 68, *69-71;* Hanov's tables of force, 58; kinds of, 59; local persistent, 59-61; measurements of direction and speed, 58-59, 129, *143,* 154, *164-165;* medieval chart, *139;* naming of, 57; orographic (mountain-bred), 16, 61, 85, *98;* regional persistent, 59, 61-62; upper-atmosphere, measuring, 59, 158, 175, *177,* 178; of vernal equinox, *56;* weather-map symbols for, *table* 168
Wind scoops, Hyderabad, *120-121*
Wind vanes, 58-59, 142, *143,* 154, *165*
Wise, John, 134-135
World Meteorological Organization (WMO), 85, 160
Wren, Sir Christopher, 129, 142; his weather-clock, *129*

X

X-rays, in atmosphere, 175

Z

Zephyr, 16
Zephyros, wind, 16, *59*
Zonda, wind, 61, 85

PICTURE CREDITS

The sources for the illustrations which appear in this book are shown below. Credits for the pictures from left to right are separated by commas, from top to bottom by dashes.

Cover—Dmitri Kessel.

CHAPTER 1: 8—Burk Uzzle from Black Star. 10, 11—Drawings by Otto van Eersel. 12, 13—Bottom drawings by Nicholas Fasciano. 15—Drawing by Patricia Byrne. 17—Susan McCartney from Photo Researchers, Inc. 18, 19—Werner Stoy for Camera Hawaii, Emil Schulthess from Black Star. 20, 21—Russ Kinne from Photo Researchers, Inc.—Daniel Farber from Rapho Guillumette, Noel Habgood from Photo Researchers, Inc. 22, 23—James H. Meyer—courtesy Arthur D. Little Inc. 24, 25—Brian Brake from Magnum. 26, 27—Douglass Baglin—Brian Brake from Magnum, Robert E. Lackenbach from Black Star. 28, 29—Joe Scherschel, Eliot Elisofon—C. G. Maxwell from Alpha Photos. 30, 31—Daniel Farber from Rapho Guillumette. 32, 33—Mike Roberts from Photo Library Inc.

CHAPTER 2: 34—Courtesy NASA. 36—Drawings by Nicholas Fasciano. 39—SCALA courtesy Museo Di Storia Della Scienza, Florence. 40—Drawing by Nicholas Fasciano. 43—Burton McNeeley. 44, 45—Weather Bureau, Miami, Florida—Charles Moore from Black Star. 46, 47—Charles Moore from Black Star—Brad Patten, Ted Russell. 48, 49—Dr. R. H. Simpson. 50—Ted Russell. 51—Courtesy NASA. 52, 53—Drawings by Otto van Eersel. 54, 55—Maps by Otto van Eersel, Flip Schulke from Black Star.

CHAPTER 3: 56—The New York Public Library. 58—Left drawing by Matt Greene. 60, 61—Drawing by Matt Greene. 63—Drawings by Nicholas Fasciano. 65—The New York Public Library, Rare Book Division. 67—Werner Stoy for Camera Hawaii. 68—Myron Davis—drawing by Otto van Eersel. 69—Drawing by Otto van Eersel. 70, 71—Top left Lee Johnson; right drawing by Matt Greene. 72—Leonard McCombe. 73—Drawings by Otto van Eersel. 74—Eric Schaal—Victor H. Waldrop. 75—Map by Otto van Eersel. 76, 77—Drawings by Otto van Eersel, Boeing Aircraft Co.—Vincent J. Schaefer. 78, 79—Drawing by Matt Greene, D. C. Jones.

CHAPTER 4: 80—Francis Miller. 82—Map by Patricia Byrne. 84—Drawing by George V. Kelvin. 85—Drawing by Nicholas Fasciano. 86—Drawing by Matt Greene. 87— Drawings by Arnold C. Holeywell and Otto van Eersel. 88—Ciccione from Rapho Guillumette, courtesy Bibliothèque Nationale. 89—Culver Pictures. 91—Art Rickerby from Pix. 92, 93—Loomis Dean—Juliana Wang from Photo Researchers, Inc., Vincent J. Schaefer, Stephen Collins from Photo Researchers, Inc., Vincent J. Schaefer (2), Alfred Eisenstaedt, Richard A. S. Schleusener of Colorado State University. 94—Drawings by Paul Calle. 95—Drawing by Paul Calle, overlay by Adolph E. Brotman. 96—Vincent J. Schaefer—R. S. Scorer. 97—Drawing by Paul Calle, overlay by Adolph E. Brotman. 98—Drawing by Otto van Eersel. 99—Carl Mydans. 100, 101—Map by Charles Mikolaycak—drawings by Arnold C. Holeywell. 102—Top Dr. Harold Edgerton; bottom Gordon Tenney. 103—Gordon Tenney. 104—Drawings by Otto van Eersel. 105—Yitka Kilian.

CHAPTER 5: 106—Hank Walker. 108—Courtesy Bancroft Library at the University of California, Berkeley. 109—Courtesy The National Museum, Tokyo. 115—Emil Schulthess from Black Star. 116, 117—Lawrence Battey from Rapho Guillumette (2), Dick Smith—Aerofilms Ltd. from Fairchild Aerial Surveys. 118—Pierre Boulat. 119—A. Y. Owen—St. Louis *Post Dispatch*. 120, 121—Carlo Bavagnoli—

Peter Stackpole, Ewing Galloway. 122, 123—Carl Mydans, Peter Stackpole, Walter Sanders. 124—K. O. Nash; Radiophysics Division CSIRO—courtesy Project Cirrus. 125—John Dominis.

CHAPTER 6: 126—Courtesy The Burndy Library. 128—Courtesy Johns Hopkins Press from *The History of the Barometer* by W.E.K. Middleton. 129—Derek Bayes courtesy Royal Society, London. 131—Culver Pictures—The Bettmann Archive. 132—Derek Bayes courtesy The Royal Institution. 133—The New York Public Library, Rare Book Division. 134—Henry Groskinsky, The New York Public Library. 135—Eddy van der Veen courtesy Charles Dollfus. 136—Henry Groskinsky, Cambridge University Press. 137—U.S. Department of Commerce ESSA and The I.B.M. Corporation. 139—Erich Lessing from Magnum courtesy Österreichische National Bibliothek. 140, 141—Painting by Tang-Too, courtesy The Knights of Columbus Film Library at St. Louis University. 142—Derek Bayes courtesy Science Museum, London—painting by Gaspere Martellini, SCALA. 143—Derek Bayes courtesy Science Museum, London, David Lees courtesy Museo di Storia della Scienza, Florence. 144—Alan Clifton courtesy The Royal Aeronautical Society. 145—Henry Groskinsky courtesy The New York Public Library from *Travels in the Air* by James Glaisher, published by Richard Bentley & Son, New Burling St., London, 1871. 146, 147—Emmett Bright from a sketch by E. Jervis in *La Campagne de la Crimée*, published by Layard, Brussels, 1855—The Bettmann Archive, Culver Pictures, U.S. Department of Commerce ESSA. 148—Fotograf Wilse, Oslo—courtesy The American Meteorology Society from the Carl G. Rossby Memorabilia. 149—Courtesy Massachusetts Institute of Technology except bottom right courtesy The American Meteorology Society from the Carl G. Rossby Memorabilia. 150, 151—Alan W. Richards—courtesy Dr. Jules Charney, Burton Glinn from Magnum.

CHAPTER 7: 152—Courtesy U.S. Department of Commerce ESSA. 154—Courtesy Johns Hopkins Press from *The History of the Barometer* by W.E.K. Middleton. 155—Drawing by Nicholas Fasciano. 157—Drawings by Matt Greene. 159—Culver Pictures. 161—Ted Russell. 162, 163—Ted Russell, drawings by Ron Becker—drawing by Otto van Eersel. 164, 165—Top left Ted Russell; bottom right drawing by Ron Becker. 166—Ted Russell. 167—Drawing by Ron Becker. 168—Weather map © 1964 by The New York Times Company, reprinted by permission. 169—Map by Leo and Diane Dillon—Ted Russell. 170, 171—Ted Russell.

CHAPTER 8: 172—J. R. Eyerman. 175—Drawing by Dave Allen. 176—Map by George V. Kelvin. 177—Drawing by Nicholas Fasciano. 179—Aldo Durazzi. 181—Ivan Massar from Black Star. 182, 183—Maps by Lowell Hess and Matt Greene; background by Leo and Diane Dillon. 184, 185—J. R. Eyerman except top left, Charles Moore from Black Star. 186—Gordon Tenney. 187—Ivan Massar from Black Star. 188, 189—Left Gordon Tenney; right Ivan Massar from Black Star. 190, 191—Boulder Laboratories, National Bureau of Standards. 194—Royal Meteorological Society except top right, Jesse Lunger from Black Star. 195—Royal Meteorological Society. Back Cover—Patricia Byrne.

A
STONEHENGE
BOOK

PRODUCTION STAFF FOR TIME INCORPORATED

John L. Hallenbeck (*Vice President and Director of Production*), Robert E. Foy, Caroline Ferri and Robert E. Fraser
Text photocomposed under the direction of Albert J. Dunn and Arthur J. Dunn

XXX